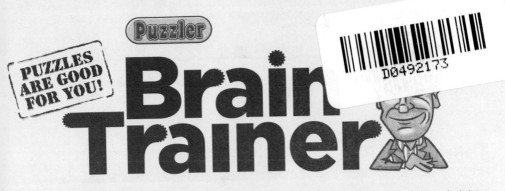

PUZZLES ARE GOOD FOR YOU!

Puzzler Brain Trainer

Ian Robertson is a neuroscientist, trained clinical psychologist and world expert on brain rehabilitation.

Currently Professor of Psychology at Trinity College, Dublin, he has worked in Cambridge, Toronto and London, and is a regular keynote speaker at conferences on brain function throughout the world.

Ian has written for The Times and British Medical Journal, and made numerous TV appearances. His many scientific articles and books include the leading international textbook in his field, the popular science books Mind Sculpture and Mind's Eye, and the successful self-help manual – Stay Sharp with the Mind Doctor.

Ian's most recent research has demonstrated how it is possible to improve mental function among normal, older people.

Ian

Ian Robertson

www.alligatorbooks.co.uk

Published in 2009 by Alligator Books Limited, Gadd House, Arcadia Avenue, London N3 2JU. Retain this address for future use.
The Alligator logo is a registered trade mark of Alligator Books Limited.

Printed in China.

SAVE 15%*

3 easy ways to subscribe:

☎ 0844 844 0079† Hotline open: Mon-Fri 0800-2000 Overseas callers please call +44 (0)1795 414686

🖥 www.puzzler.com ✉ simply fill in the form below

✂

Puzzler Brain Trainer Magazine Subscription

PLEASE COMPLETE THIS FORM AND SEND IT TO: Puzzler Brain Trainer Magazine, PO Box 453, Sittingbourne ME9 8WT

☐ Yes, I would like to save 15% off my subscription (13 issues for ~~£34.37~~, £29.21)*

Your details:

Mr/Mrs/Miss/Ms (Please delete as appropriate)

FIRST NAME

SURNAME

ADDRESS

_____ POSTCODE

TELEPHONE No.

EMAIL

Gift Recipient's Details (if applicable)

☐ I enclose a cheque/PO made payable to Puzzler Media Ltd.
OR Please debit my MasterCard/Visa/Maestro:

Card no.

Valid from ☐☐☐☐ Expires end ☐☐☐☐

Issue no. (Maestro only) ☐☐ Date ☐☐☐☐

Signature

*Subscriptions will start with the next available issue. UK offer only. Overseas rates are available on request. †The maximum call charge for BT customers is currently 5p per minute. Charges from other phone companies may vary. **Offer closes: August 31, 2011.**

Puzzler Media Ltd (or via its agents) may wish to contact you with relevant offers or for marketing purposes. Please tick the box if you **DO NOT** want to be contacted for these purposes, by post or telephone ☐

Puzzler Media Ltd (or via its agents) may wish to contact you by email or SMS with relevant offers or for marketing purposes. Please tick the box if you agree to this: ☐

PUZZLER MEDIA WILL NOT SELL YOUR INFORMATION TO ANY THIRD PARTIES.

PBTTP093

D0492173

Fitword

When all of the listed words have been placed correctly in the grid, which one is left over?

3 letters
All
Coo
Ego
Let
Odd
Opt
Rid
Tat
Tot

4 letters
Abut
Amid
Arty
Eden
~~Hymn~~

Racy
Rate
Riot
Type

5 letters
Array
Laced
Money
Panel
Troll
Uncut

6 letters
Dahlia
Dulcet

H Y M N

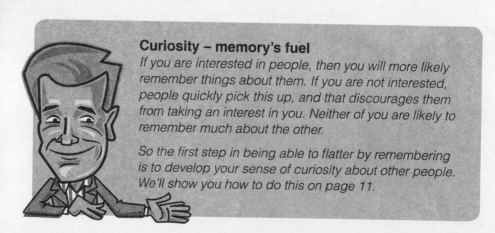

Curiosity – memory's fuel

If you are interested in people, then you will more likely remember things about them. If you are not interested, people quickly pick this up, and that discourages them from taking an interest in you. Neither of you are likely to remember much about the other.

So the first step in being able to flatter by remembering is to develop your sense of curiosity about other people. We'll show you how to do this on page 11.

Codeword

Can you crack the code and fill in the crossword grid? Each letter of the alphabet makes at least one appearance in the grid, and is represented by the same number wherever it appears. The four letters we've decoded should help you to identify other letters and words in the grid.

24		26		19		24	14	21		24		10		15
9	19	13	19	1	15	6		11	15	19	6	15	25	25
13		15		5		7		15		6		15		5
15	24	6	20	19	17		11	22	25	21	15	6	19	24
6				25		8				19				16
8	26	18	9	26	19	6		21	19	23	16	24	1	19
		9		6		26		24		15		2		25
5	26	9	15		25	7	18	2	7		10 (J)	19 (I)	2 (L)	21 (T)
28		15		18		15		15		19		8		
23	24	6	19	1	15	6		1	26	21	11	19	1	17
23				11				21		15				8
18	1	24	20	24	8	15	25		25	1	26	26	4	15
21		3		16		13		24			25		1	24
15	5	2	19	16	25	15		5	2	19	12	18	15	25
6		15		22		6	18	15		2		25		22

A B C D E F G H ~~I~~ ~~J~~ K ~~L~~ M N O P Q R S ~~T~~ U V W X Y Z

1	2 L	3	4	5	6	7	8	9	10 J	11	12	13
14	15	16	17	18	19 I	20	21 T	22	23	24	25	26

TIP

When tackling this puzzle, remember ETOANRISHI. These are the most widely used letters in English. If a number crops up frequently in this puzzle, it's likely to be one of these.

Logical

How quickly can you figure out what's what?

The Puzzler Virtual Puzzle Tournament has reached its conclusion, with the top three players being announced.

Cara didn't come first, and her online name wasn't Trixie. Hathor was Tara's pseudonym, and she came next after Sara, whose alter ego wasn't Questor.
Which player had which pseudonym and which place did they gain?

Moon Dog

Moon Dog's been out and about again. Which of the ten shadows is his true shadow?

Mix & Match

This mixed-clue crossword will get you thinking in lots of different ways. Riddles, anagrams, word association and general knowledge are all included.

ACROSS

1 If something's in this underground feature, it's possibly forthcoming (8)

5 A LAG shows up at a swimming show (4)

9 Bury some painters (5)

10 Abridge a short story by the sound of it (7)

11 Word coming before Box, Kit and Shed (4)

12 If you've got this, you'll get a new date daily (8)

14 Shake TERM OR quiver (6)

15 PAY ROD in mocking imitation (6)

18 In the open, an innkeeper is produced (8)

20 Heavy metal guide (4)

23 Being heartless, UPS LOCAL disturbance (7)

24 Word following Born, Never and Yet (5)

25 Cut it in the park (4)

26 Where there's a dance floor with space to score! (8)

DOWN

1 Word following Check, Pin and Match (5)

2 THE POOL damaged a feature of bad roads (7)

3 Traditional knowledge (4)

4 Anagram of RECANT (6)

6 Get a medal when A DRAW is thrown up (5)

7 Throw up in GALLERY, being hypersensitive (7)

8 Football team's weapons (7)

13 Line you can't see over (7)

14 Anagram of CAPITOL (7)

16 Confusing OREGON with A herb (7)

17 Nasty and unpleasant sensation ends after initially having disgust (6)

19 Word linking Fur, Par and Stairs (5)

21 MINED up cotton cloth (5)

22 Go by sea – sounds like a bargain event! (4)

Staircase

When these business terms are correctly fitted in the rows of the grid, another such term will appear down the diagonal staircase.

BUYING

COMPANY

DEVALUE

GOODS

OUTPUT

SERVICE

STOCK

Hide and Seek

How quickly can you identify the squares in which each of the numbered shapes appears?

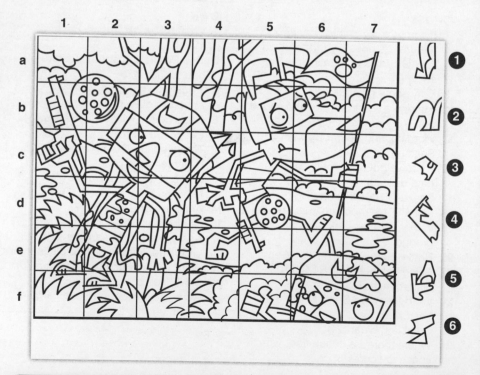

Dateline

Work out the answers to the clues to discover the date in the shaded space – a significant date in education and equality. Calculators strictly forbidden!

1		2		3		4		☐
		6				7		
☐						☐	10	
				11			12	
	13		14			1☐		
16			17					1☐
1☐		2☐				21		
		22		23				
24						2☐		

ACROSS

1 4 Across + 17 Across
4 Half of 13 Down
6 13231 + 14383 + 15613
8 Hours in 3 weeks
9 Anagram of 1 Down
11 8496 ÷ 118
12 Bull's eye in darts
13 Mystery date
16 432 ÷ 27
17 212 + 303 – 424
19 A third of 10863
21 712 – 427 + 398
22 101010 – 17834
24 17 x 3 dozen
25 4 Across x 6 + 6

DOWN

1 493 x 6
2 15 Down – 6 Across – 23 Down
3 Weeks in a year
4 13 Down – 17 Across
5 12121 – 8431
7 813 + 914 + 1101
10 2286 ÷ 9
11 79 x 9
13 Pounds in 19 stones
14 17 cubed
15 7 Down x days in May
16 Anagram of 19 Across
18 7 Down – 8 Across
20 A quarter of 1128
23 684 ÷ 57

Spaghetti Loopy

Which of the pieces of spaghetti on toast has been cut from the main piece? Remember to match the pattern and the shape.

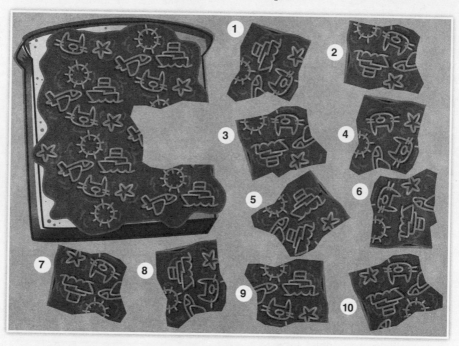

Futoshiki

Fill the blank squares so that each row and column contains all the numbers 1, 2 and 3 in the smaller grids, and 1, 2, 3 and 4 in the larger grid. Use the given numbers and the symbols that tell you if the number in the square is larger (>) or smaller (<) than the number next to it.

Number Jig

All but one of these numbers will fit in the grid. How quickly can you get the numbers placed, and which is left over?

3 Digits
318
360
374
408
412
859

4 Digits
2088
2482
2828
3265
3478
3482

4150
4259
4529
5172
5428
6150
6710
6715
6819
6828
9186

5 Digits
36628
37668

42207
44079
76672
97408

7 Digits
1852647
5264781

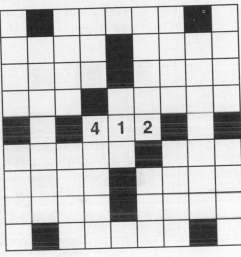

Arroword

Just follow the arrows to write your answers in the grid.
A handful of anagram clues will get you thinking differently. The shaded letters will spell out a word you'll need for a later puzzle, so try to commit it to memory.

Culpable		Playing-card		Yachting event		Painting, drawing etc		Busybody	SPINET (anagram)
Impure, soiled								Entertain	
Every single one		BALM (anagram)		ORGAN (anagram)					
				Function	MOATS (anagram)				
Goad, mock							Submit (to a vote)		
					SHEET (anagram)				
Fitness centres	Second Greek letter						Travelling salesman		

Codeword

Can you crack the code and fill in the crossword grid? Each letter of the alphabet makes at least one appearance in the grid, and is represented by the same number wherever it appears. The five letters we've decoded should help you to identify other letters and words in the grid.

19		9		18		22	19	7		2		16		18
25	14	18	18	4	15	19		18	6	10	15	26	13	21
25		4		6		17		25		14		13		18
13	10	23	24	10	26		19	23	3	5	18	23	15	2
14			15		4				15					10
12	18	7	12	14	13	20		1	18	26	18	25	15	23
	19		18		13		13		24		10			18
5	18	8	11		25 F	14 R	13 O	26 N	23 T		13	26	10	4
19		18		19		23		1		19		24		
7	13	14	5	12	5	11		13	10	4	23	15	26	24
17				12				26		20				11
19	8	15	19	14	15	18	4		9	15	23	3	18	14
16		23		18		12		22		14		18		19
18	21	2	10	4	18	12		18	8	15	12	18	26	23
14		3		4		11	18	23		26		5		18

A B C D E F̸ G H I J K L M N̸ Ø P Q R̸ S T̸ U V W X Y Z

1	2	3	4	5	6	7	8	9	10	11	12	13 O
14 R	15	16	17	18	19	20	21	22	23 T	24	25 F	26 N

TIP
If you look for repeated patterns of letters, you may find it easier to work out parts of the code. For instance, the word reading down the starter letter N has two sets of three letters repeated, and there's just one possibility for this word. A good place to look for repeated patterns is at the end of words – 18 4 occurs more than once, and so too 15 26 24.

Puzzler Brain Trainer

10

Developing your curiosity

As I've mentioned before, the human brain is the most complicated thing in the known universe. Nothing, anywhere, is more strange and complex. Something else I've mentioned before: your brain is physically shaped and changed by experience from the womb through until death.

This means – as the Nobel Prizewinner Gerald Edelman has recently pointed out – that each individual human being is totally and utterly unique. They have to be, because if you take the 100 billion brain cells together with the millions of different experiences that every individual has, then the resultant set of possible combinations is mathematically unique.

So, you are utterly and totally unique in the universe, and so is every other person that you meet. Every person you meet deserves your total attention for as long as you are with them, and also your curiosity: who are they, what drives them, what are they interested in, what are they fearful about, what do they believe in… etc etc?

If you decide to take this on board, then you are well on the way to remembering things about other people. If you are not curious about others, then you are unlikely to be motivated to learn things about them. Depending on what you want out of life and work, that can be detrimental to your achieving those things.

Staircase

When these types of medicine are correctly fitted in the rows of the grid, another such term will appear down the diagonal staircase.

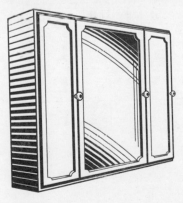

ANTACID
EMETIC
INSULIN
POTION
SALVE
SERUM
STYPTIC

Forget yourself for a moment – part 1

Memories are like bridges – you need scaffolding when you are building them.

One of the most important pieces of scaffolding in our brains is our own self. Answer these questions:

- *Remember the last time you ate an orange.*
- *Where were you and what were you doing when the 9/11 attacks happened?*
- *When did you last travel in a bus?*
- *Who was prime minister when you left secondary school?*

These questions are simply designed to draw your attention to scaffolding and memories.

We'll explore this further on page 25.

Mind the Gap

Can you place a well-known three-letter word in the spaces of each row to complete the seven-letter word? Do it correctly, and the shaded letters should spell out something bright.

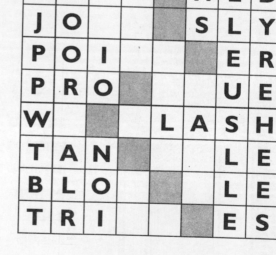

U	N				H	E	D
J	O				S	L	Y
P	O	I				E	R
P	R	O				U	E
W				L	A	S	H
T	A	N				L	E
B	L	O				L	E
T	R	I				E	S

HAVE A GO!

Pathfinder

Beginning with WHITE, and moving up, down, left or right, one letter at a time, can you trace a path of eighteen colours?

V	A	O	S	W	H	I	H	A	L	P
E	L	N	M	T	N	T	E	Z	E	U
N	C	R	I	A	E	M	E	N	I	R
D	E	U	L	B	G	A	R	A	R	P
E	R	I	O	I	N	E	T	M	A	L
M	A	L	N	R	A	U	L	U	R	E
B	E	I	O	C	M	A	U	S	H	A
T	R	M	R	H	D	A	Q	S	K	K
U	E	V	E	R	L	O	G	E	T	I
R	S	I	S	E	L	E	N	D	I	V
Q	U	O	C	A	R	T	A	I	R	I

Sudoku

Use your powers of reasoning to place numbers in the grid, so that each row, each column and each 3x3 block contains the numbers 1-9.

6								2
	7		8		2		9	
2			5		6			3
7				9				8
	9		1		5		3	
5	6		7	8	4		2	1
			3		7			
	5		2		1		6	
		2				7		

If you'd like to tackle a harder version of this puzzle, go to **puzzler.com**

Wrestle Table

The MC has forgotten which wrestlers are fighting each other in the quarter-finals of the WNW (We're Not Weird) wrestling championship. From the pictures and comments below, can you pair up the finalists?

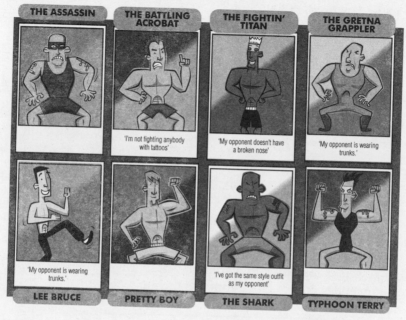

THE ASSASSIN

THE BATTLING ACROBAT
'I'm not fighting anybody with tattoos'

THE FIGHTIN' TITAN
'My opponent doesn't have a broken nose'

THE GRETNA GRAPPLER
'My opponent is wearing trunks.'

LEE BRUCE
'My opponent is wearing trunks.'

PRETTY BOY

THE SHARK
'I've got the same style outfit as my opponent'

TYPHOON TERRY

Lose a Letter

Cross out one letter in each square to leave a completed crossword. You may have to think ahead to rule out some red herrings along the way.

Missing Links

The three words in each of these clues have a fourth word in common, and that's your answer. For instance, the clue to 7 Across 'Formula • Sided • Way (3)' gives you the answer ONE (Formula One, One-sided, One-way).

ACROSS

1 Body • Dinner • Guide (4)
4 Club • Course • Crazy (4)
7 Formula • Sided • Way (3)
8 Cadet • Probation • Warrant (7)
10 Forest • Lone • Texas (6)
12 Bitten • Collar • Market (4)
13 Entrance • Nerves • Paper (4)
15 Cut • Lozenge • Sore (6)
19 Model • Parrot • Victim (7)
20 Faced • Radio • Timer (3)
21 Farm • Poker • Press (4)
22 Junk • Scotland • Stick (4)

DOWN

2 Going • Indian • Liner (5)
3 Hail • Lime • Mason (5)
4 God's • Token • Wrap (4)
5 Anaesthetic • Authority • Derby (5)
6 Beside • Please • Suit (8)
9 Chain • Gut • Time (8)
11 Boots • Bubble • Wine (3)
12 Coat • Fake • Seal (3)
14 Hidden • Stripping • Valuable (5)
16 Comb • Moon • Suckle (5)
17 Hebrides • Limits • Space (5)
18 Boggling • Open • Reader (4)

Word Builder

Using the nine letters provided, can you answer these clues? Every answer must include the highlighted letter B. Which type of street uses all nine letters?

D	U	V
A	B	E
L	O	R

5 Letters
Cutting edge
Unstimulated
Dwelling
Over
Hurrah!
Bakery product

6 Letters
Twice
Of words
Part of speech
More plucky
Russian currency unit
Risked

7 Letters
Large rock
Long lasting

8 Letters
Toiled

Backwords

The answers to this crossword are all here, along with extra letters where the black squares should be. Can you black out any unwanted letters to leave a grid that matches the clues (which are out of order)? The finished grid will have full symmetry.

SYMMETRY

ACROSS

- Liquid
- Lost your footing
- Bother
- Locking pin
- From the Netherlands
- Car race
- Fuel used for cooking
- Underwear item
- Burnt remains
- Rub painfully
- Singleton
- Spoil, disfigure
- Adam's biblical mate
- Slaver, drivel
- Bow and arrow users
- Fetch

DOWN

- Hoodwink
- Use money
- Humbled
- Object
- Dried grass
- Savage
- Warder
- Personal journal
- Boat paddle
- Appoint (by ballot)
- Small horse-like animal
- Put a question
- Hole of a needle
- Poem addressed to a person
- Peaty land
- Underwater swimmer

B	R	A	N	D	I	S	H	O	N	E
O	A	S	L	I	P	P	E	D	A	Y
G	A	S	P	A	R	E	D	E	V	E
E	B	O	B	R	I	N	G	R	I	N
R	A	L	L	Y	E	D	U	T	C	H
A	S	S	U	M	E	T	A	P	I	C
C	H	A	F	E	L	D	R	O	O	L
L	E	A	F	L	U	I	D	O	U	R
A	D	O	S	E	L	V	E	A	S	H
I	P	A	R	C	H	E	R	S	P	A
M	A	R	I	T	O	R	O	K	E	Y

Picture Pair

How quickly can you spot the two identical pictures?

Six Pack

Can you place digits in the empty triangles, so that the numbers in each hexagon add up to 25? Only single digits between 1 and 9 can be used, and no two numbers in any hexagon may be the same.

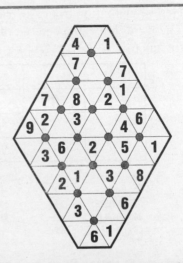

Memory Jog

This is the first part of a three-part Memory Jog, so it will be a bit of a test, but it should also show you how repeating things in your memory fixes them more strongly in your mind.

Below is a compass, with various places named in relative locations. Spend two minutes concentrating on the compass image, then cover it up and see if you can recreate it.

Once you've tackled part one, you'll find part two on page 23.

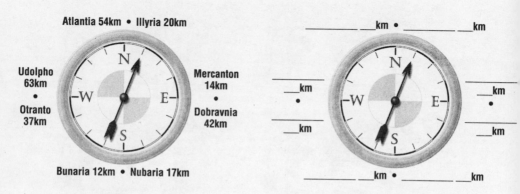

Atlantia 54km • Illyria 20km

Udolpho 63km
•
Otranto 37km

Mercanton 14km
•
Dobravnia 42km

Bunaria 12km • Nubaria 17km

_____ __km • _____ __km

___km
•

__km
•

___km

__km

_____ __km • _____ __km

Drop Quote

Here's a quotation from American writer James Thurber on the next life. The words have dropped out of position into the columns. Can you restore the quote?

				BELIEFS	
,	IT				
I					TO
,		VERY,			.

IF	I	~~VERY~~	WILL	FEW	DOGS
HEAVEN	AND	IS	THAT	~~BELIEFS~~	~~TO~~
IMMORTALITY	~~IT~~	KNOWN	VERY	GO	PERSONS
+	HAVE	HAVE	ANY	CERTAIN	ABOUT

Sudoku

Use your powers of reasoning to place numbers in the grid, so that each row, each column and each 3x3 block contains the numbers 1-9.

		5		1				
1	9	7	6					
				3	9			
			4	9		6		
			5		8	2		1
5	8			6	2		3	
	3						8	5
	5	6	3				4	
9			8				6	

Mobile Quotes

We've put three quotations in code, using the numbers on a mobile keypad. So, for instance, the first letter of the first quote could be T, U or V.
Can you work out what Agatha Christie said?

"843 2378 8463 86 7526 2 2665 47 94453 968'73 36464 843 347437."

"4 366'8 84465 632377489 47 843 668437 63 468368466 – 468368466, 46 69 6746466, 274737 34732859 3766 43536377, 76774259 2576 3766 52946377. 86 7283 6637353 8768253."

"4 5453 548464. 4 4283 766384637 2336 945359, 337724746459, 2288359 647372253, 722533 9484 767769, 288 8476844 48 255 4 78455 5669 78483 237824659 8428 5878 86 23 25483 47 2 47263 84464."

Mobile keypad:
1 | 2 ABC | 3 DEF
4 GHI | 5 JKL | 6 MNO
7 PQRS | 8 TUV | 9 WXYZ
* | 0 | #

Alpha-Beater

Every letter of the alphabet has been removed from this crossword once. How quickly can you put all 26 back? Use the A-Z list to cross off letters as you use them.

S		L		U	R			U	
C	H	E		S		O		N	
A									
	R		D	A	L		W		O
		T						I	
O	N					O		C	E	D
	I			B					O
	C	U		E		E		U	I
	K				A	D		P	E

A	B	C	D	E	F	G	H	I	J	K	L	M
N	O	P	Q	R	S	T	U	V	W	X	Y	Z

Set Square

Place one each of the digits 1-9 in each grid to make the sums work. We've put in some of the numbers to start you off. Sums should be solved from left to right, or from top to bottom.

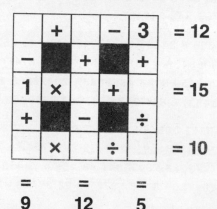

Elimination

All but two of the listed words fall into one of the four categories. Put these leftover words together, and what word or phrase do they make?

CATEGORIES

Satellites • Synonyms of 'GREEN' • London rail stations • Words preceding 'DOOR' (eg front)

Telstar	Marylebone	Trap	Victoria
Stop	Moon	Sputnik	Iridium
Inexperienced	Stage	Leafy	Fire
Paddington	Common	Barn	Euston
Verdant	Naïve	Full	
Stable	Waterloo	Explorer	

Kim's Game

Ready for a memory challenge! Study these objects for 30 seconds, then turn the page.

Kim's Game

See page 21 before having a go at these questions. Looking at the objects on this page, can you tell what has changed from the previous page?

1 Which two original hieroglyphs have been removed?

2 Which two new hieroglyphs have been added?

3 What other three changes have been made to the hieroglyphs?

Spot the Difference

Can you spot the six differences between these two pictures?

Memory Jog

Here's part two of the Memory Jog. It's a map of the island we referred to on page 18. What we'd like you to do here is fill in the place names that are missing: you have to recall the names we gave, and work out where they should be placed.

Once you've tackled part two, make sure you've got it right – check against the solutions pages, and if you've made any mistakes, correct them. You're now ready for part three – try to fix as much information in your mind from the entire map as you can, and turn to page 44 for part three's questions.

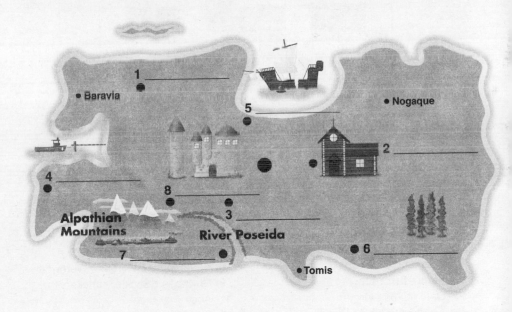

Three to One

You'll have to think ahead to complete this crossword. You have a choice of three words to put in each space, but which will fit with its neighbours?

ACROSS
 1 Fire • Jeer • Mess
 4 Bore • Oche • Once
 7 Ego • Emu • Ewe
 8 Asphalt • Shellac • Slowest
10 Eating • Excite • Intake
12 Semi • Taxi • Topi
13 Oars • Orbs • Orgy
15 Anorak • Screed • Shrunk
19 Faulted • Haulage • Scuttle
20 Car • Tar • Toe
21 Defy • Feel • Melt
22 Ewer • Roll • Ward

DOWN
 2 Enact • Exert • Iliac
 3 Reset • Risen • Stark
 4 Beat • Oboe • Pipe
 5 Cameo • Erase • Hyena
 6 Behemoth • Desirous • Werewolf
 9 Chickpea • Stickler • Trickery
11 Abs • Any • Icy
12 Sir • Too • Tor
14 Blush • Gauze • Roust
16 Cider • Hedge • Widow
17 Extol • Recur • Untie
18 Salt • Stay • Tart

Forget yourself for a moment – part 2

It's amazing the detail you can remember about little episodes from your life: I remember eating an orange last Saturday morning, for instance. Thinking about t hat makes me remember who was sitting round the table, that the weather was very windy and that I had planned to go out that afternoon but didn't.

I can only remember these details because they are all attached to the scaffolding of my self, my long-term stored memories and my goals, needs and desires.

Very young children who have not yet developed that strong sense of self don't remember details and episodes because of this. They live in the moment, but memories don't stick to them because there isn't a strong scaffolding of self for them to cling to.

So what's this got to do with remembering facts about other people? Well, most of us are quite self-centred, maybe a little self-engrossed. So when someone tells me that they went on holiday to southern Italy, I have a tendency to immediately think about the time I went to southern Italy on holiday. In other words, I am taking their fact and sticking it onto my self-scaffolding. This means that I am less likely to remember this fact about them than if I tried to build a little scaffold based on them – this utterly one-of-a-kind-in-the-universe person. So, to remember facts about people, you need to try to leave your self behind and try to put yourself in their shoes. Automatically this will provide a new scaffold which will make you much more likely to remember a few things about them.

Mini Jigsaw

Fit the pieces in the grid to spell a printing term in each row.

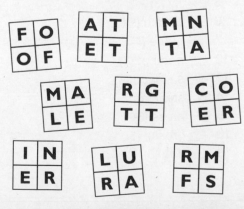

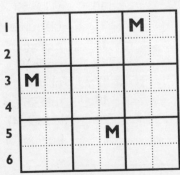

First Thoughts

Fill in the blank in each clue to make a well-known word or phrase, then write your answers in the grid. We've solved one clue to start you off.

ACROSS

1 ___ crawly (6)
4 ___ pole (4)
8 ___ bag (3)
9 ___ table (7)
10 ___ Wise (5)
11 ___ instrument (5)
13 ___ cake (5)
15 ___ pads (5)
17 ___ pill (7)
19 ___ rule (3)
20 ___ ladder (4)
21 ___ boxing (6)

DOWN

1 ___ reef (5)
2 ___ English (7)
3 ___ pois (5)
5 ___ fly (3)
6 ___ Britain (5)
7 ___ stone (4)
12 ___ combat (7)
13 ___ sausage (5)
14 ___ steak (4)
15 ___ press (5)
16 ___ grease (5)
18 ___ dog (3)

The Great Escape

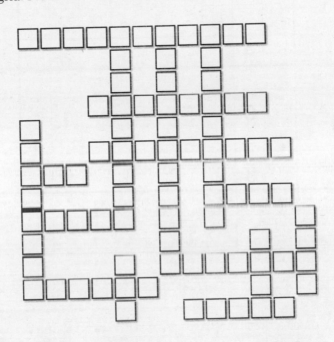

HAVE A GO!

Have you started thinking of your summer hols yet? I have – but it's dream rather than reality in my case. For you fortunates who have got the chance of going away, here's a list of holiday essentials to fit in the grid. No starters are needed this time.

3 letters
REP
SUN

4 letters
ROOM
SAND
VISA

5 letters
GUIDE
PLANE

6 letters
TICKET

7 letters
SANDALS

8 letters
CURRENCY
PASSPORT

9 letters
CAMCORDER
INSURANCE
ITINERARY

11 letters
ATTRACTIONS
DESTINATION

Sudoku

Use your powers of reasoning to place numbers in the grid, so that each row, each column and each 3x3 block contains the numbers 1-9.

			2					
	9		1		7	2		
	4			5			3	
		1				5		
	9		5				1	
7			6	2				4
	8	2			6		9	
1		4		8	3			
	3		1					

Arroword

Just follow the arrows to write your answers in the grid. Are the anagram clues a help or hindrance?

Vital elements	Quick, nimble	SEVERER (anagram) ▼		And so on (abbr) ▼		Ice-cream flavouring ▼		Cleopatra's snake ▼	▼
▶	▼								
IDLER (anagram)		ISLE (anagram)		REED (anagram)		Weekly earnings		Narrow Scottish valley	
▶		▼		▼				▼	
					Hairpiece ▶				Full collection
Large bright meteors									▼
▶									
					Great joy ▶				
Sir __ Redgrave, rower	GRANTEES (anagram) ▶								

Prints Charming

Which of the numbered fingerprints matches each of the fingertips on the left?

Word Sleuth

Use your powers of deduction to work out our four-letter mystery word. The four different letters in the mystery word can be worked out by comparing the scores of the clue words. Every letter in a clue word that is in the mystery word is scored with a circle, black if the letter is in the correct place, grey if it isn't. So, for example, WILD shares two letters with our mystery word, with both of them in the correct position.

CLUE WORD	Score
W I L D	●●
F O R D	●○
F O I L	●●○
L O R E	●○
F O L D	●●○
F I L E	●○

MYSTERY WORD

●●●●

Skeleton

Despite appearances, this is a regular crossword, with a fully symmetrical grid. So the small amount of information we've given (numbers and black squares) will help a great deal in filling in the full grid pattern.

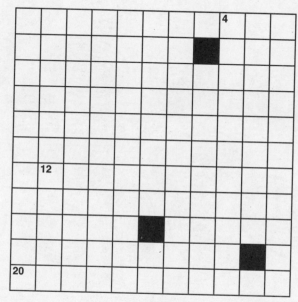

ACROSS

1 Aspiration
3 Extravagant publicity
6 ___ O'Connor, *Countdown* host
8 Greek holiday island
9 Concede
10 Lively, high-spirited
12 Drawing back in disgust
17 Place of refuge
18 Benefactor
19 Gaming cube
20 *Happy* ___, US sitcom
21 Capital city of Norway

DOWN

1 Put in pawn
2 Heat-resistant glass ovenware
4 Middle East country of which the chief port is Aden
5 Dines
6 Astonish
7 Profanity
10 Sound-sensitive organ
11 Style of wrestling for two teams of two
13 Diplomatic messenger
14 Ben ___, Scotland's highest peak
15 Garden outbuilding
16 Group of three people

Logical

Try solving this logical problem in your head before putting pen to paper.

Three pen-pals, Charles, Joy and Robina, each entered their local Mayday Feast competition. In their letters they discussed their recipes. From the information given, can you say who lived where and which two ingredients their recipe included?

Charles' recipe included oranges but neither hazelnuts nor beetroot, although beetroot was one of the ingredients used by the person in Dundee. Robina, who wasn't from Wrexham, used cream in her recipe, but not carrot. The peach and beetroot combination wasn't made in Lisburn.

Knot or not?

Which two of the frogs will have tied a knot in their tongues and which two will not?

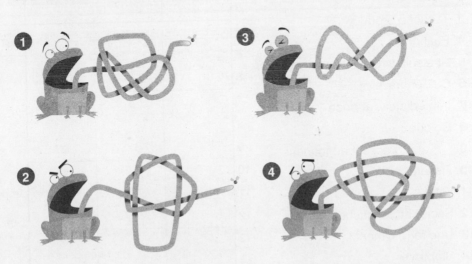

Jigsaw

Use the jigsaw pieces to recreate this completed crossword. We've only listed clues for the rows of Across words, but the pattern of the grid should help you, being symmetrical from top right to bottom left.

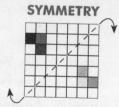

ACROSS

1 Copy, imitate

2 Implored

3 Tobacco product

4 Pushchair

5 At a ship's rear

6 Cut, engrave

7 Immediately, at once

8 Colour

9 ___ and graces, haughtiness

10 Fisherman

11 Total

12 Secret store, cache

13 Due for payment

14 Slop over

15 Room illumination

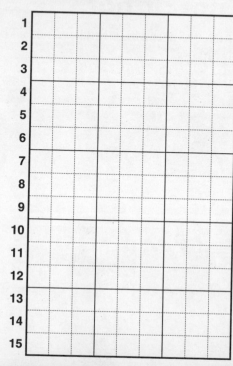

Pattern Maker

Which one of the numbered squares should replace the question mark to follow the logical pattern in each of these three sequences?

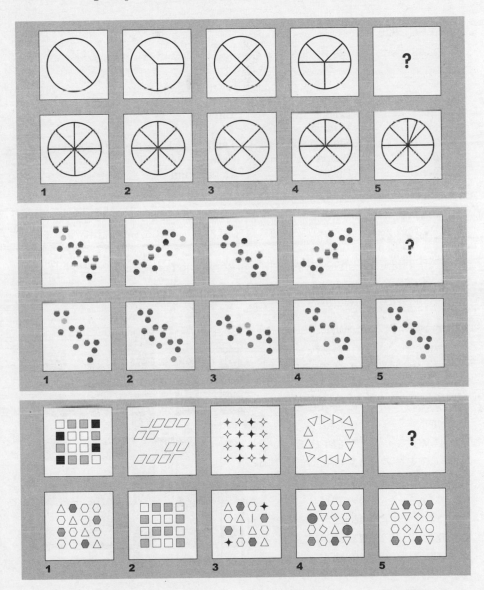

Elimination

All but two of the listed words fall into one of the four categories. Put these leftover words together, and what word or phrase do they make?

> **CATEGORIES**
>
> Inventors • Types of puzzle • Watercourses • Computer hardware items

Riddle	River	Anagram	Creek
Stream	Chip	Cable	Hole
Edison	Faraday	Brook	Mouse
Key	Stephenson	Dunlop	Cryptogram
Marconi	Button	Disk	
Crossword	Rivulet	Conundrum	

Mix-up

The clues here are all anagrams. Just unscramble the letters to get the answers. Some words have more than one anagram, so you'll need to see which fits with its neighbours.

ACROSS

1 PACER
4 FLAIR
7 NAP
8 BUN
9 NET
10 LAME
11 AGREE
14 LEASE
16 FLEA
18 OWL
20 TAP
21 MID
22 ROOTS
23 RENTS

DOWN

1 TRAP
2 RESCIND
3 PANEL
4 BRIEF
5 CAT
6 ENROLS
12 GRENADE
13 LEADER
15 TALES
16 LOUTS
17 MEAN
19 HOW

Fair Play

Here's a test of your visual memory. Study the scene below for two minutes, paying particular attention to where in the scene the various elements appear. The puzzle continues on the next page.

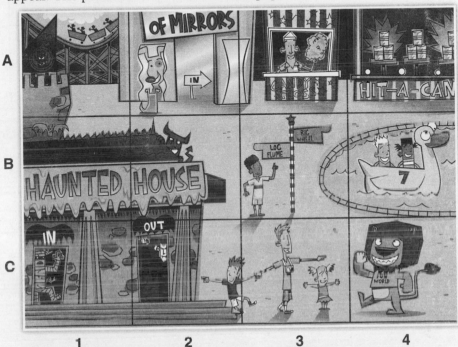

Add Up

If the number in each circle is the sum of the two below it, how quickly can you figure out the top number? You may have to work up and down the pyramid. See if you can climb the third pyramid in fewer seconds than the number you reach at the top.

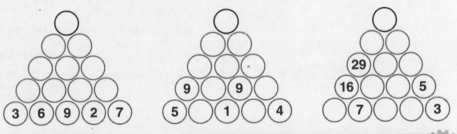

Fair Play

Can you write the number of each of these elements of the picture in the correct square of the grid?

1 **Camera**

2 **'Out' sign**

3 **Dog**

4 **Candyfloss**

5 **Mummy**

6 **Lion costume**

7 **'LOG FLUME' sign**

8 **Rollercoaster**

9 **The number 7**

10 **Red devil**

	1	2	3	4
A				
B				
C				

Draw cartoons in your mind

Of course not everyone you meet is fascinating – some can be really dull – but even that dullness can be interesting if you pay attention to it.

Cartoonists are geniuses at picking one or two characteristics of appearance or posture that just capture a person: Tony Blair's teeth or Margaret Thatcher's hair, for instance.

Memory works a bit like that – it stores memories using a few features that are like labels on library bookshelves. If you can exaggerate in your mind's eye one or two features of the person you are talking to, then you will remember them much more easily.

Take the dull person you have just been talking to at the party. You can, if you want, make a cartoon in your mind's eye of that person as a clerk in a Dickensian office, sitting on a high stool patiently writing numbers into an enormous leather book. Visualise him with a stoop if you like, meekly climbing down from the stool at the end of a long day just transcribing numbers.

If you make a cartoon-strip tale like this, you are creating a set of scaffolding that is separate from your self. You are building a little story, and our brains find it much easier to hang facts onto stories.So, this person may be dull, but maybe could help you out in business. Entertain yourself with the cartoon, and attach a couple of facts about the person to your cartoon: two teenage children, for instance, impatiently bored on a long dull Sunday afternoon beside their very dull father. He told you his wife's name is Ella: visualise her as an extroverted dancer and hear him in your mind's ear whispering, 'Ella, calm down, please.'

Do you get the idea? We all love stories, but our brains love them even more. Learn the habit of telling yourself stories about the people you meet. These can be true stories based on what they tell you, or made-up stories like the dull clerk: it doesn't matter, as what you are doing is building scaffolding on which to hang facts about the people you meet.

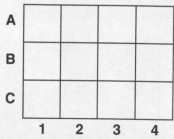

Dilemma Fitword

Can you fit all the listed words into the two grids? You'll need to do some thinking ahead, and jumping between grids to crack this one. Turn the page for a starter hint.

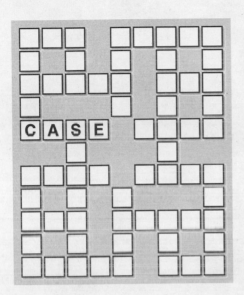

3 letters	RUN	KNIT	BROWN	THONG
BAG	TOE	LILY	GREET	TONIC
BAR	TOO	LONG	HASTE	TUBER
BUD		SNAP	LEDGE	VISIT
EAR	**4 letters**	SNUB	NABOB	
EEL	~~BOOK~~	TEST	NASAL	**7 letters**
OLD	BRAN	VANE	NINJA	NERVOUS
OWN	BUNG		NYLON	SERIOUS
RED	~~CASE~~	**5 letters**	PASTA	SINUOUS
ROO	EPEE	BATCH	PLEAT	SIRLOIN
		BATON		

Wheels & Cogs

When Caveman Keith turns his cog, will the pointer move towards the right or left dinosaur?

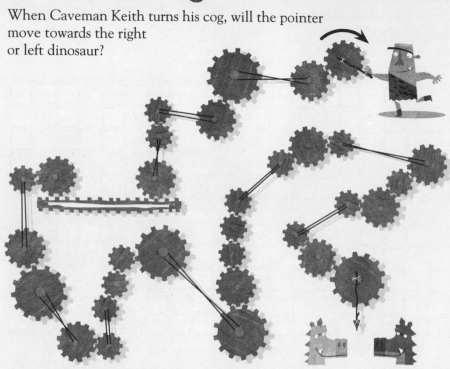

Wheely Good

I wonder where we'd be without the wheel. Closer to home, no doubt. There are sixteen things with wheels (and not all of them the obvious wheel!) for you to find in the grid – hopefully you'll be on a roll.

U	N	I	C	Y	C	L	E	R	N	B
D	M	E	D	N	A	T	I	I	M	I
E	P	N	R	S	Z	R	A	V	O	C
Y	K	T	A	T	C	R	A	S	P	Y
E	O	I	O	C	T	O	U	C	E	C
S	J	W	B	U	O	I	O	L	D	L
E	X	J	E	R	T	A	L	T	C	E
T	F	K	T	C	O	O	C	A	E	S
A	C	H	A	I	R	T	H	H	H	R
K	Q	S	K	T	M	F	O	I	L	B
S	E	G	S	M	A	R	P	M	N	S

PAGE 37 DILEMMA FITWORD TIP
If you can't work out which seven-letter word to place from the starters, fill in any definite letters in the word and cross-check with the possibilities for intersecting words.

Word Builder

Using the nine letters provided, can you answer these clues? Every answer must include the highlighted letter P. Which audience member uses all nine letters?

S	E	T
A	P	T
R	O	C

5 Letters
Cloaks
Bulbous juicy fruits
Extra
Gum
Physical activity
Non-poetic writing

6 Letters
Harry ___, fictional character
Abrade
Classical music dramas
Cleric, minister
Viewpoint
Advertising sheet

7 Letters
Brewing vessels
Boots' protective elements
Floor coverings
March, demonstration
Harbour, docks town

8 Letters
Safeguards, defends

Memory Jog

Before tackling this, you should have solved Wrestle Table on page 14. This is a straightforward, though challenging, memory jog – can you put the correct name to the correct wrestler? Once you've filled in the names, refer back to page 14 to see how well you did.

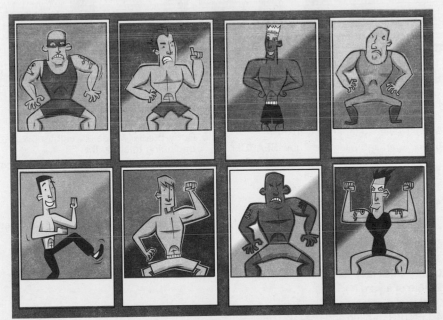

Mix & Match

You'll have to think just a little bit differently with this mixed-clue crossword. Riddles, anagrams, word association and general knowledge are all included.

ACROSS

1 Anagram of STROBE (6)
5 Residential area on the outskirts of a town (6)
8 Word coming before Down, Eye and Out (4)
9 Past lover – alter and swap (8)
10 Flanagan and Allen somehow SEARCH underneath here in song (6)
11 Anagram of CORDON (6)
12 This couple sounds fruity (4)
14 Word following Chicken, Dry and Long (3)
15 European's somewhat Napoleonic (4)
16 Club chauffeur (6)
18 Military pageant (6)
20 Very small fairy-tale character (3,5)
22 36th of a yard (4)
23 Wizard bird (6)
24 I ENTER, broken and unbroken (6)

DOWN

2 Word linking Every, Wise and Worldly (5)
3 Massacre meat man (7)
4 Accountant's part account re: a sure return on investment (9)
5 In biology and medicine, a pouch (3)
6 Body-builder raises a weight, now beginning to show this (5)
7 Cloth toy produced by LAG LORD (3,4)
11 Copper artist (9)
13 Breathing space? (3,4)
15 ___ *Games*, Harrison Ford film (7)
17 Word coming before Organ, Resources and Statistics (5)
19 Wilde's award (5)
21 Vase is displayed in our new museum (3)

Killer Sudoku

The normal rules of Sudoku apply. Place a digit from 1-9 in each empty square so that each row, column and 3x3 block contains all the digits from 1-9. In addition, the digits in each inner shape (marked by dots) must add up to the number in the top corner of that box. No digit can be repeated within an inner shape.

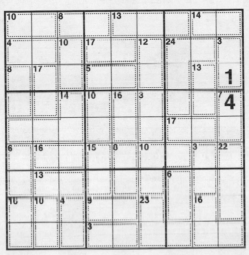

Lettersets

Complete the crossword grid using the letters listed for each row and column. Cracking this one relies on anagram-solving and cross-referencing between Across and Down words.

ACROSS
1 ACMRTUW
2 AEERSUU
3 AFNNPRU
4 AEFŁLPTU
5 NORTU
6 ABBEŁLOO
7 DDEOUWY
8 FGILORW
9 AEFKLLY

DOWN
1 BCFFFFUU
2 AILNUU
3 AELNRTUY
4 EŁLOPS
5 EKOPRUW
6 AAŁOTW
7 BELLMNOU
8 ADORRT
9 ADEEGRWY

Missing Links

The three words in each of these clues have a fourth word in common, and that's your answer. For instance, the clue to 8 Across, 'Context • Flow • Venn (7)' gives you the answer DIAGRAM (Context diagram, Flow diagram, Venn diagram).

ACROSS

1 Folk • Super • Worship (4)
4 Basin • Car • Hog (4)
7 Boot • Dead • Peg (3)
8 Context • Flow • Venn (7)
10 Blossom • Picker • Tomato (6)
12 Book • House • Wide (4)
13 Block • Rage • Ring (4)
15 Blades • Coaster • Steam (6)
19 Cheese • Hospital • Industry (7)
20 Brazil • Cracker • Shell (3)
21 Kettle • Kit • Major (4)
22 Head • Stomach • Tooth (4)

DOWN

2 Bald • Eyed • Legal (5)
3 Form • Tall • Working (5)
4 Away • River • Under (4)
5 Comic • Landing • Sunset (5)
6 Eel • Guitar • Shock (8)
9 Ethnic • Report • Shareholder (8)
11 Blooded • Carpet • Squirrel (3)
12 Linseed • Painting • Tanker (3)
14 Life • Noon • Thought (5)
16 House • Soap • Singer (5)
17 Box • Hour • Time (5)
18 Beach • Date • Sunday (4)

Make other links

We remember things by linking them to what we know already. We also remember things better when our brains work on the material that we have to remember.

Read this list of letters once, cover them, and test yourself on your memory for them:

b f s l f a t t c i o t w s

How did you do? If you really only read it once, you probably got about half of the letters right, maybe a little more or less.

Now, read the following sentence and then test yourself on your recall of the first letter of each word. Try to visualise the scene as you read the words.

Big fish swallow little fish as the tide comes in over the warm sand.

Now can you remember the fourteen letters? You should have remembered significantly more than the first time. This is because your brain finds it much easier to remember things that are connected to words and pictures that you already have stored in your memory.

How do you apply this to remembering facts about people?

Well, take their names. Suppose someone is called Linda. You can entertain yourself while talking to Linda by trying to make up a sentence from the letters of her name:

Likes Ireland niece dancer actor.

This assumes that Linda told you she had a nice holiday in Ireland and that her niece is a dancer in a west end show. It would help if you made a mental picture of Linda prancing on the stage with her niece, possibly wearing a green shawl and attempting Irish dancing.

Or Simon could be Silent I must (witter) on.

It's hard at first to play these one-person party games, but I can assure you they are great fun, even at the most boring party!

What's more, if you play them, you will definitely remember facts about other people, and that can be a very, very useful thing to do.

You'll find a recap of all that we've considered on page 47.

Square Eyes

Two squares in this scene are identical, though they may not be the same way up. Which are they?

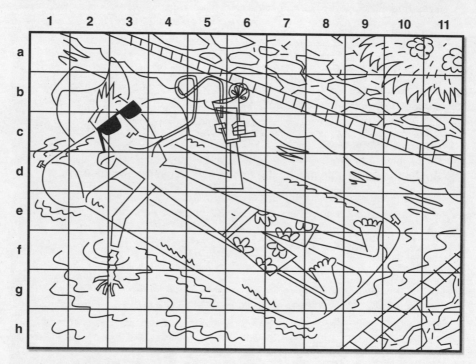

Memory Jog

The answers to these questions are found on page 180.

1 Which is the southernmost town?

2 Which place is closest to the shipwreck?

3 Which town is immediately below Baravia?

4 What is the name of the river?

5 Which place is most central on the island?

6 Which island feature is closest to Dobravnia?

7 What is the name of the mountain range?

8 The palace and bell-tower are in which town?

Codeword

Can you crack the code and fill in the crossword grid? Each letter of the alphabet makes at least one appearance in the grid, and is represented by the same number wherever it appears. The three letters we've decoded should help you to identify other letters and words in the grid.

4		2		10		10	21	21		24		19		12
16	15	25	26	18	4	14		23	15	20	20	25	26	4
16		22		25		5		25		20		24		22
15	11	4	14	13	6		24	20	3	15	14	22	4	14
14				10		10				14				10
22	14	10	24	22	15	14		23	14	10	7	24	13	6
		13		4		22		8		13		20		10
12	10	24	13		3	24	17	24	4		1	10	24	13
24		9		26		21		11		13		9		
23	15	26	18	25	23	22		11	10	24	26	4	21	22
5				3				6		9				1
4	17	10	23	22	24	26	9		21	8	4	13	11	4
				T	I	N								
14		2		24		4		10		22		10		26
4	20	10	26	10	22	4		1	24	13	18	23	10	22
18		14		13		18	25	4		6		4		6

A B C D E F G H ~~I~~ J K L M ~~N~~ O P Q R S ~~T~~ U V W X Y Z

1	2	3	4	5	6	7	8	9	10	11	12	13
14	15	16	17	18	19	20	21	22	23	24	25	26
								T		I		N

Boxwise

Can you place the three-letter groups in the boxes, so that neighbouring boxes always make a six-letter word, like PAR-DON or DON-ATE? We've placed one group to start you off.

AIL   ING
ASY   LUM
~~BAR~~   PRE
ENS   QUE
FER   RET
FIL   TER

Number Jig

All of these numbers will fit in the grid. How quickly can you get the numbers placed?

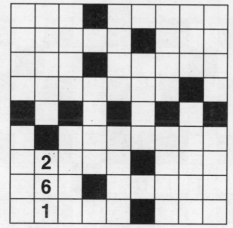

3 Digits	4 Digits	7016	32019
~~261~~	1049	7309	32020
350	1066	8394	32589
351	1943	9194	41019
851	2013		52584
855	2382	**5 Digits**	
861	3379	11789	**7 Digits**
956	5062	12784	4825309
999	5362	21683	7626321

Writing Wrongs

There are five pictures here, but there's something wrong with each of them. Can you figure out what the error is in each of them?

1
2
3
4
5

Memory for facts about people – recap

As we've discovered through this issue, it is quite simple to achieve a great improvement in your memory for facts about people. The four strategies we've explored are simple and effective.

- *Be curious about people - every person is unique*
- *Forget yourself – this way you'll create new scaffold for remembering facts about other people*
- *Draw cartoons in your mind – use images to create a story in your mind. This is another way to create scaffold and 'fix' details in your mind.*
- *Make other links – use words and pictures to fast-track your memory. Try mnemonics using initial letters, or make a sentence from the letters in somebody's name.*

Fitword

When all of the listed words have been placed correctly in the grid, which one is left over?

3 letters
Act
All
Chi
Fat
Off
Pay
Ply
Sip
Via

4 letters
Dodo
Flit
Home
Hoot

Oast
Skim
Skit
~~Used~~

5 letters
Aback
Aloof
Frill
Mufti
Shirk
Shock
Skied

6 letters
Defame
Doffed

Do you get things done?

As with all these things, your starting point should be to work out where you are and where you should be. So, we've got five simple questions for you – circle the number that best fits how you feel. When you're finished, add up the numbers and go to page 52.

• When something needs to be done, I just do it and get it over with.	* Usually 3	Sometimes 2	Hardly ever 1
• I have lots of little things hanging over me that I never get round to dealing with.	* Usually 1	Sometimes 2	Hardly ever 3
• I tend to put things off and think, 'I'll do that later.'	* Agree strongly 1	Agree somewhat 2	Disagree 3
• My friends and colleagues know that if I say I'll do something, it will get done.	* Agree strongly 3	Agree somewhat 2	Disagree 1
• I think with regret of things I would like to do but never seem to do.	* Agree strongly 1	Agree somewhat 2	Disagree 3

Jigsaw

How quickly can you figure out what's what? Use the jigsaw pieces to recreate this completed crossword. We've only listed clues for the rows of Across words, but the pattern of the grid should help you, being symmetrical from top right to bottom left.

SYMMETRY

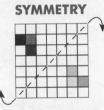

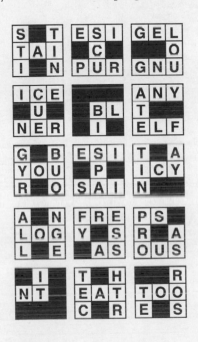

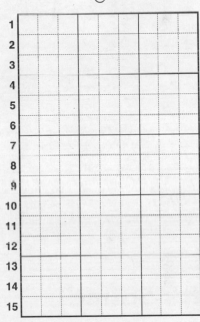

ACROSS

1 Arm muscle
2 Second person singular
3 Exacting
4 No matter which
5 Calf's cry
6 Fairy-like being
7 Take (exams) again
8 As well • Chilly

9 Reject disdainfully
10 Hair-setting agent
11 Contaminate
12 Ox-like antelope
13 Strong scented plant of the iris family
14 Piece of wood cut for the fire
15 Set upon, attack

Too Close a Shave

Which of the nine reflections is the true reflection of Razor Ryan?

It's Sound!

There are fifteen styles of music to be found within the grid – told you it's sound! How quickly can you find them?

G	Z	E	P	J	H	L	Y	F
R	S	I	A	R	E	P	O	O
U	G	G	B	P	A	V	S	L
N	C	O	S	W	V	P	I	K
G	E	O	V	O	Y	H	U	J
E	G	B	U	L	M	B	A	S
K	A	I	A	N	E	M	Z	W
N	R	C	K	B	T	Z	C	I
U	A	E	O	L	A	R	T	N
P	G	P	N	J	L	F	Y	G
C	L	A	S	S	I	C	A	L

Mix & Match

This mixed-clue crossword will get you thinking in lots of different ways. Riddles, anagrams, word association and general knowledge are all included.

ACROSS

1 Burn fuel and discover another fuel (8)
5 Long film some depicted (4)
9 Anagram of SPATE (5)
10 Large stone (7)
11 It's mad in March (4)
12 Word linking Moon, Mornington and Red (8)
14 Anagram of NAILED (6)
15 It shows the fairest of them all in panto (6)
18 Anagram of TARRAGON (8)
20 Word coming before Come, Due and Throw (4)
23 NINE VEG are tossed at the end of the day (7)
24 Model AILED, fell ill (5)
25 Quick punctuation? (4)
26 Stroke palm's reverse! (8)

DOWN

1 You can do this to a crab or a cold (5)
2 Take this when tormented with PAIN, SIR! (7)
3 Word following Broad, Down and Type (4)
4 Royal Bertha entrapped a royal prince (6)
6 Anagram of DRAPE (5)
7 A priest endlessly joins alternative guardian (7)
8 Chase a pastime (7)
13 Pact to veto advantage (7)
14 Road to nowhere (4,3)
16 I ARRIVE confused at the coast (7)
17 Elgar's variations are a mystery (6)
19 Rods that can't net some elver eels (5)
21 Governed with straight lines (5)
22 Word coming before Chocolate, Maid and Thistle (4)

How did you score?

If you scored between 10 and 15, you're pretty good at getting things done. There's always room for improvement, so you may find some of the tips we have in this issue of Puzzler Brain Trainer *useful.*

A score of between 6 and 9 is fair, but definitely suggests there are improvements you can make to your effectiveness at getting things done. You probably waste some time thinking about things you have to do, and as a result feel hassled and/or rushed. Read on for more tips.If you notched up no more than 5 points, you probably feel preoccupied or lacking in motivation quite a lot of the time. My tips can make a huge difference to you: nothing uses up mental energy more than having lots of unfinished business cluttering up your brain. Take on my tips to discover how to get more out of life.

Now turn to page 57..

Hide and Seek _____

How quickly can you identify the squares in which each of the numbered shapes appears?

Dateline

Work out the answers to the clues to discover the date in the shaded space – a significant date in personal finances. Calculators strictly forbidden!

1		2		3		4		□
		6			7			
□					□		1□	
				11			12	
	13		14			1□		
16			17					1□
1□		2□				21		
		22		23				
24						2□		

ACROSS

1. 483 + 217 − 3 Down
4. 1 Across plus a century
6. 1305 x legs on a spider
8. A third of 1053
9. 20,202 − 8778 − 1695
11. Square root of 1 Across
12. 469 ÷ 7
13. Mystery date
16. Pounds in 3 stone, or 3 Down reversed
17. 13 Down − 11 Down
19. 2635 +3749 +2701
21. Last 3 numbers of 2 Down
22. 10,649 x half a dozen
24. 11 x 23 Down
25. Months in a year x days in February 2008

DOWN

1. 43,617 ÷ 7
2. 101,101 − 39,924 − 51
3. Two dozen
4. 439 + 10 Down
5. Anagram of 7 Down
7. 99,340 ÷ 20
10. A quarter of 1072
11. Days in 30 weeks
13. 20% of 1100
14. 1234 + 1574 + 2345
15. Half of 180,286
16. 4 Down x days in a week
18. 50 pence pieces in £1314
20. Minutes in a day − 577
23. 8 Across − 10 Down

Futoshiki

Fill the blank squares so that each row and column contains all the numbers 1, 2 and 3 in the smaller grids, and 1, 2, 3 and 4 in the larger grid. Use the given numbers and the symbols that tell you if the number in the square is larger (>) or smaller (<) than the number next to it.

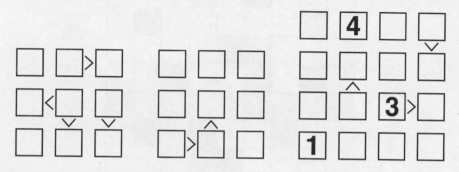

Number Jig

All but one of these numbers will fit in the grid. How quickly can you get the numbers placed, and which is left over?

3 Digits
157
164
594
657
929
954

5264
5676
7296
7612
7822
9260
9264

4 Digits
1232
1764
1816
2360
2626
2820
3215
3279
3619
5210

5 Digits
51462
55364
66067
67347
94096
97370

7 Digits
2798237
6792538

Codeword

Can you crack the code and fill in the crossword grid? Each letter of the alphabet makes at least one appearance in the grid, and is represented by the same number wherever it appears. The five letters we've decoded should help you to identify other letters and words in the grid.

4		5		5		5	22	1		7		5		5
7	4	3	9	11	4	11		9	26	9	26	15	4	11
9		4		11		16		15		5		11		21
2	5	22	2	5	10		12	15	5	7	9	20	15	9
20				8		5				4				22
22	8	18	18	15	4	11		2	9	1	21	5	10	9
	5		2		11		16		11		15		10
11	18	8	10		21	9	0	9	4		24	0	10	12
8		10		5		12		22		2		19		
19	20	5	2	1	4	10		2	20	17	15	9	10	4
13				20				23		9				1
4	15	20	14	8	4	10	2		4	10	2	20	1	19
26		1		10		20		5		11		20		20
2	5	9	10	2	4	7		17	16	4	4	25	4	7
11		2		11		11	8	4		2		4		23

Decoded letters shown in grid: 2=T, 17=W, 10=I, 11=N, 9=S

A B C D E F G H ✗ J K L M ✗ O P Q R ✗ ✗ U V ✗ X Y Z

1	2	3	4	5	6	7	8	9	10	11	12	13
	T								I	N		
14	15	16	17	18	19	20	21	22	23	24	25	26
			W									

Decoded: 9 = S, 10 = I, 11 = N, 17 = W, 2 = T

TIP
One of the skills required to complete a codeword puzzle is spotting patterns of letters. Don't be lulled into a false sense of security, however. We've given you the number 9 as one of the starters this time, and there are three words in this grid that end with a '9' – not one of the more common word endings in English. Try to recall this whenever you come across a codeword.

Arroword

Just follow the arrows to write your answers in the grid. A handful of anagram clues will get you thinking differently.

ATTARS (anagram) ▼		Cook with oil ▼		Religious ministers ▼		Family vehicle ▼		Lowers in rank	STAPLE (anagram)
RETRACE (anagram) ►						▼		Guy, man	▼
Cooling device		__ Batty, Compo's paramour		Latin American dance ►			▼		
►			▼	__ Basinger, US actress	Goblin-like creature ►				
Capital city of Japan ►				▼		Part of your foot ►			
►				Stinks					
Hindu woman's dress	SPAM (anagram) ►					Complete collection		

Staircase

When these household fixtures and fittings are correctly placed in the rows of the grid, another will appear down the diagonal staircase.

BASIN

BLIND

CISTERN

CURTAIN

KEYHOLE

PILLOW

RUNNER

What's wrong with putting things off?

Putting off doing things clutters up your brain – it's a little like tying weights to your legs. It slows you down, mentally. You know how it is if you're expecting someone to call at your house: it's more difficult to concentrate – part of your brain is listening for the doorbell and it checks noises outside to see whether it's the person arriving.

*Getting something done, on the other hand, declutters your brain – it clears a little space from an important part of your mind and leaves more room, for instance, to stimulate your brain with Puzzler Brain Trainer exercises and puzzles. Getting something done also provides a sense of satisfaction, and even a feeling of pleasure. This is linked to a little spurt of an important brain chemical messenger called **dopamine**. This in turn makes you feel more positive and motivated.*

That's just one reason why you should ask a busy person to get something done. Busy people, assuming they're not TOO busy and therefore stressed, get lots of satisfaction from jobs well done. Their brains are forever giving themselves mental gold stars in the form of little extra amounts of the reward chemical dopamine.

StepRiddle

At my start, I'm young horses, or guns in the old Wild West.

Change my first and I become locks on the door to your nest.

When my second letter's changed, I'm used to keep up pairs of trousers.

At the next, change my next, and I'm defeats; rhythmic drum noises.

When my fourth is adapted, I can be grizzly or polar creatures.

At the last, change my last, and I can cover a face's features.

What was I, what did I become, and what did I turn out to be?

Missing Links

The three words in each of these clues have a fourth word in common, and that's your answer. For instance, the clue to 1 Across, 'Card • Family • Secret (5)' gives you the answer RECIPE (Recipe card, Family recipe, Secret recipe).

¹R	E	²C	I	³P	E	■	4	5	■	6
	■		■		■	7			■	
8			■	9						
	■		■		■		■		■	
10					■	11		12		
■	■	■		■	■		■		■	■
13			14		15					16
	■		■		■		■		■	
17		18			■		■	19		
	■		■		■		■		■	
20				■	21					

ACROSS

1 Card • Family • Secret (6)
4 Beauty • Blind • Check (4)
8 Eyed • John • Skin (3)
9 Eye • Finance • Education (7)
10 New • Tall • Working (5)
11 Leaf • Tree • Syrup (5)
13 Harrier • Marigold • Salt (5)
15 *Financial* • *Hard* • Tables (5)
17 Dive • Tail • Up (7)
19 Tempered • Will • Wind (3)
20 Cabin • Cut • Neck (4)
21 Attendant • Charter • Path (6)

DOWN

1 Clock • Digital • Talk (5)
2 Caves • Cheese • Gorge (7)
3 Chase • Sand • Weight (5)
5 Cock • Green • Sweet (3)
6 Fore • Upon • With (5)
7 Clip • Feature • Set (4)
12 Blood • Iron • Up (7)
13 Box • Pop • Room (5)
14 Concert • Porter • Town (4)
15 Rail • Roller • Tea (5)
16 Banana • Pin • Second (5)
18 Battle • Pick • Pole (3)

Backwords

The answers to this crossword are all here, along with extra letters where the black squares should be. Can you black out any unwanted letters to leave a grid that matches the clues (which are out of order)? The finished grid will have central symmetry, from top right to bottom left.

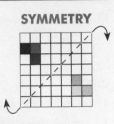

SYMMETRY

A	L	W	I	S	T	E	R	S	E	C
C	L	I	P	P	E	D	S	W	O	O
T	E	L	S	E	G	G	R	A	N	A
S	O	L	V	E	Y	E	I	G	H	T
O	V	O	I	D	E	S	C	A	L	E
B	O	W	A	Y	A	M	A	R	I	D
U	N	S	U	R	E	O	P	E	N	S
B	U	R	S	T	A	V	I	P	E	R
B	R	O	W	O	N	I	T	L	Y	E
L	A	W	E	P	A	N	C	A	K	E
Y	E	S	A	S	H	G	U	Y	A	L

ACROSS

- Legal system
- Potato-like root
- Romance
- Lower the head in greeting
- Pruned
- Shrove Tuesday dish
- Number of tentacles on an octopus
- Free, disencumber
- Adder's other name
- Find the answer to
- Explode

DOWN

- Nippy
- Second match
- Bobbin
- Burglar's loot
- Performs in a film
- Lids
- Weeping ___, tree
- Champers
- Brink
- Arguments
- Touching, emotional
- Covered (in)

Dilemma Crossword

The clues for these crosswords have been mixed up. As you solve them, you'll need to work out which answer goes in each grid.

ACROSS

1 Key maker • Mouth-cleaning device

7 Horrify • Make (a person) laugh

8 Noon meal • Chew

10 Tip, point • Fat used to make puddings

11 Secondary or smaller • Jail

14 Animals of pasture • Shoe liner

15 Barbecue rod • Saintly ring of light

17 Pixie-like • Ingested

19 Cider's fruit base • Resonant metallic sound

20 Accuracy • Nervous excitement

DOWN

2 Tyrannise • Very rich

3 Row • Scottish tartan garment

4 Recollection • Rope-carrying wheel

5 Soft metal • Is able to

6 Animal living off another • Slaughter, carnage

9 Country's history • After-effect of alcohol

12 Highest variety of voice • Hair-cleaning liquid

13 Celestial body such as Neptune • Private hospital

16 Pole on a ship • Winning tennis serves

18 Road-surfacing material • Sticky boxed fruit

Sudoku

Use your powers of reasoning to place numbers in the grid, so that each row, each column and each 3x3 block contains the numbers 1-9.

1			9			7		
								1
	6			5	3	8		4
	9			6				8
1			8		2			
	5			7				2
	4			1	9	2		6
								9
	8			2			3	

Mobile Quotes

We've put three quotations in code, using the numbers on a mobile keypad. So, for instance, the first letter of the first quote could be T, U or V. Can you work out what was said?

"843 625328 63 8447 26673848466 47 668 86 23 6326 86 843 567377 288 86 3463 2 946637. 843 7762377 62537 968 6326 2322873 968 438 3787872833. 5437 8876 87 86734327733, 9327464 843 97664 2568437, 7464464 688 63 8863 263 968 226 348437 729, '4663 562,' 263 728766473 8436 67 8355 8436 843 87884, 263 766384637 843 87884 47 737234833 27 6326."

"4 42836'8 3663 26984464 727842852759 42774. 427746377 86 63 47 448464 76632639 32573 46737 263 668 365569464 8476844. 8428'7 42774. 8355464 7663 489 67 7663 4475 946'83 468 9376 825368 8428 8439 4283 9376 825368 22882559 47 2 54636377."

"4 36 2 268753 63 4863733 77377-877 2 329 288 4 42836'8 2336 86 2 496 46 93277."

1	2 ABC	3 DEF
4 GHI	5 JKL	6 MNO
7 PQRS	8 TUV	9 WXYZ
*	0	#

Alpha-Beater

Every letter of the alphabet has been removed from this crossword once. How quickly can you put all 26 back? Use the A-Z list to cross off letters as you use them.

E	◼	Y		◼	R	A	◼	A	
	R		Y	◼			O	R	D
I					T			I	◼
◼	O	U	G	A	R	◼	T	A	R
◼		R		Y	◼				
	O			B			Z		R
◼			I		E		Z		
◼	E	M	O	◼		E		I	C
	N				E	Y	◼	E	

A	B	C	D	E	F	G	H	I	J	K	L	M
N	O	P	Q	R	S	T	U	V	W	X	Y	Z

Set Square

Place one each of the digits 1-9 in each grid to make the sums work. We've put in some of the numbers to start you off. Sums should be solved from left to right, or from top to bottom.

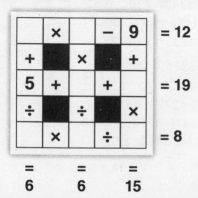

Left grid:

	×		−	9	= 12
+	◼	×		+	
5	+		+		= 19
÷	◼	÷		×	
	×		÷		= 8

= 6   = 6   = 15

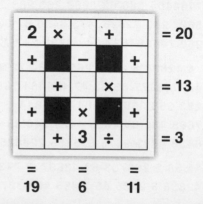

Right grid:

2	×		+		= 20
+	◼	−	◼	+	
	+		×		= 13
+		×	◼	+	
	+	3	÷		= 3

= 19   = 6   = 11

Elimination

All but two of the listed words fall into one of the four categories. Put these leftover words together, and what word or phrase do they make?

CATEGORIES

Rainbow colours • Songbirds • Art terms • Cartoon characters

Brush	Canvas	Wagtail	Pluto	Tintin
Thrush	Acrylic	Black	Swan	Yellow
Red	Wren	Model	Pastel	
Custard	Violet	Lark	Droopy	
Snoopy	Green	Blue	Yellowhammer	

Kim's Game

Ready for a memory challenge? Study these symbols for 30 seconds, then turn the page.

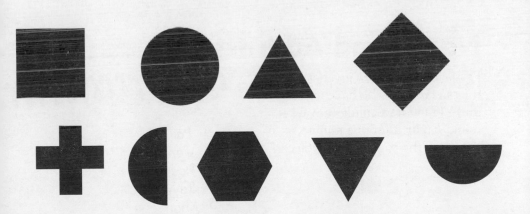

Kim's Game

See page 63 before having a go at these questions. Looking at the shapes on this page, can you tell what has changed from the previous page?

1 **Which two original shapes have been removed?**
2 **Which two new shapes have been added?**
3 **What other three changes have been made to the pictures?**

Name and Address

Postman Plato's been given a list of the ten families who have moved into a brand new cul-de-sac on his round. Study it for one minute, then turn the page to see if you can recall it.

1 Parker
2 Jones
3 Rossiter
4 Jayer
5 Khan
6 Ming
7 O'Farrell
8 Rose
9 McGowan-Smith
10 Devonport

Name and Address

Can you recall which family lives at which number? The family names have been listed alphabetically – fill in the number of the house in which they live.

- —— Devonport
- —— Jayer
- —— Jones
- —— Khan
- —— McGowan-Smith
- —— Ming
- —— O'Farrell
- —— Parker
- —— Rose
- —— Rossiter

Spot the Difference

Can you spot the six differences between these two pictures?

Face Facts

Time to face facts now – find eighteen synonyms of 'face' in the grid.

L	R	E	N	N	A	M	E	F
A	W	M	V	O	M	G	K	N
I	I	O	U	I	A	W	C	C
D	E	M	C	S	T	S	O	D
K	U	C	I	S	H	N	L	I
G	P	V	A	E	F	F	C	S
P	U	H	D	R	I	A	E	P
H	B	I	O	P	T	C	K	L
I	S	N	S	X	Y	A	O	A
Z	T	L	D	E	Z	D	O	Y
S	U	R	F	A	C	E	L	B

Memory Quiz

Here's a quiz to see how much attention you're really paying to your surroundings. No peeping!

1 What were depicted on 2007's Christmas stamps?

2 What colour is the Mr Men's Mr Strong?

3 In what year did Zara Phillips win the BBC's Sports Personality of the Year?

4 Which brand of lavatory paper is associated with puppies?

5 What are the initials of the government department responsible for collecting tax?

6 What colour is predominant on British fire exit signs?

7 In *EastEnders*, which instrument did Sonia play?

8 What is the correct spelling – occurince, occurrence, occurence or occurance?

Three to One

You'll have to think ahead to complete this crossword. You have a choice of three words to put in each space, but which will fit with its neighbours?

ACROSS

1 Skew • Skin • Used
4 Daft • Heft • Soft
7 Owe • Tea • Tie
8 Antacid • Attired • Reverie
10 Caking • Likens • Rakish
12 Book • Boos • Boot
13 Evil • Iced • Idly
15 Beaver • Loaves • Quaver
19 Grudged • Lounger • Roundel
20 Nee • Pie • Woe
21 Seed • Thud • Unit
22 Arch • Dude • Rose

DOWN

2 Knack • Speck • Stalk
3 Drain • Nears • Wards
4 Hate • Love • Save
5 Curio • Forgo • Verso
6 Courtier • Stallion • Vouching
9 Deserted • Dinosaur • Dragster
11 End • Ill • Ivy
12 Boa • Bow • Bun
14 Laugh • Learn • Lease
16 Extra • Order • Undid
17 Venom • Verse • Vowed
18 Aged • Agit • Edit

Kakuro

Simple addition and a bit of logical thinking will solve this one. You must write a digit in each white square so that the digits in each block add up to the total in the box above or to the left. 1-9 are the only digits to use and, although you may find a digit repeated in a row, it must not be repeated in the same block. We've solved one block for you.

Mini Jigsaw

Fit the pieces in the grid to spell out a cuisine and cookery term in each row.

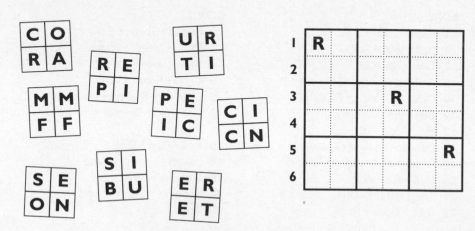

First Thoughts

Fill in the blank in each clue to make a well-known word or phrase, then write your answers in the grid. We've solved one clue to start you off.

¹C		²		³		⁴	⁵	⁶
O								
⁷M							⁸	
E								
⁹D		¹⁰			¹¹			
Y								¹²
		¹³		¹⁴		¹⁵		
¹⁶								
¹⁷				¹⁸			¹⁹	
²⁰					²¹			

ACROSS

1 ___ care (5)
4 ___ buddies (5)
7 ___ house (7)
8 ___ hand (3)
9 ___ strokes (9)
13 ___ Plot (9)
17 ___ going (3)
18 ___ bones (7)
20 ___ feed (5)
21 ___ hare (5)

DOWN

1 ___ Store (6)
2 ___ keeper (3)
3 ___ through (5)
4 ___ drinking (5)
5 ___ dick (7)
6 ___ progress (4)
10 ___ pilot (7)
11 ___ roaring (3)
12 ___ birth (6)
14 ___ art (5)
15 ___ den (5)
16 ___ club (4)
19 ___ mac (3)

Puzzler Brain Trainer

69

Phone China

Phone China, and some of the listed items could come up in conversation – they're all English words with Chinese origins. How quickly can you fit them all into the grid?

3 letters
SOY
WOK
YEN

4 letters
CHAR

6 letters
COOLIE
KOWTOW
LYCHEE
SAMPAN

7 letters
GINSENG
KUMQUAT
TYPHOON

8 letters
CHOP SUEY
CHOW MEIN
MANDARIN
SHANGHAI

Futoshiki

Fill the blank squares so that each row and column contains all the numbers 1, 2 and 3 in the smaller grids, and 1, 2, 3 and 4 in the larger grid. Use the given numbers and the symbols that tell you if the number in the square is larger (>) or smaller (<) than the number next to it.

Sudoku

Use your powers of reasoning to place numbers in the grid, so that each row, each column and each 3x3 block contains the numbers 1-9.

				9	3			5
	6		5		4	7		
		9					1	
	1						3	4
	2	3	4					9
		4		5			6	
		8	2	3		6		
1				6	5		4	
	3							

Arroword

Just follow the arrows to write your answers in the grid. Are the anagram clues a help or hindrance?

Choice foods	Wear away suit, for instance	RECLAIM (anagram) ▼	▼	Taxi	▼	MINUETS (anagram) ▼		SAP (anagram) ▼	
►		▼							
ROANS (anagram)		Close at hand		Work schedule		The Three Wise Men ▼		Paltry	
►				▼				▼	
					Mother ►				Carried out (an action)
Painted and papered (a house) ►									▼
►					_ Halliwell, Ginger Spice ►				
	DELTA (anagram)	SIDEREAL (anagram)							

Key Signatures

Which of the twelve keys will fit in each of the locks?

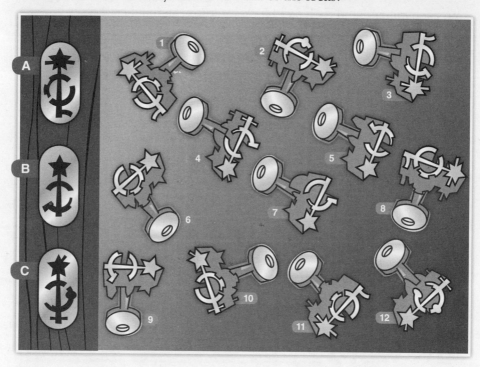

Word Sleuth

Use your powers of deduction to work out our four-letter mystery word. The four different letters in the mystery word can be worked out by comparing the scores of the clue words. Every letter in a clue word that is in the mystery word is scored with a circle, black if the letter is in the correct place, grey if it isn't. So, for example, TALE shares two letters with our mystery word, but only one of them is in the correct position.

CLUE WORD				Score
R	A	S	H	● ●
T	U	B	A	● ● ●
T	A	L	E	● ●
H	A	R	T	● ● ●
B	E	A	R	● ●
S	T	A	R	● ●

MYSTERY WORD

				● ● ● ●

Skeleton

Despite appearances, this is a regular crossword, with a fully symmetrical grid. So the small amount of information we've given (numbers and black squares) will help a great deal in filling in the full grid pattern.

SYMMETRY

ACROSS

1 Rhythmic Latin American music
4 Firmly hold
7 Ox-like antelope
8 Quotient
9 Sound, din
10 Domestic heating fuel
12 Position a vehicle
15 Watering pipe
17 Provide with
18 Robe, dress
20 Of poor quality
23 Canine
25 Asian subcontinent
26 Covent Garden entertainment
27 Afternoon refreshment
28 Wooden barrier
29 Kind of water lily

DOWN

1 Leather tie
2 Afterwards, subsequently
3 Eager, expectant
4 Firearms
5 Spanish for 'friend'
6 Fragment
11 Relating to sound
13 Commotion
14 Range of knowledge
15 That female
16 Concession
18 Deep or intense sorrow
19 Expand
21 Plain, open
22 Annual periods
23 Romantic rendezvous
24 Target in football

Logical

Try solving this logical problem in your head before putting pen to paper.

Three inventors, Joan, Nazreen and Phyllis, appeared on the entrepreneur TV show, *Bear Pitch*, and were successful in gaining the investment they were looking for. From the information below, work out which bear invested how much money in which inventor and product.

Nazreen received double the amount of money that Joan received from Rich. Rich didn't invest in the rip-proof fabric, while Luca, who invested the highest amount (£150,000), didn't put his money in the rucksack. The rip-proof fabric received an investment of £100,000, and Goldie didn't invest in the rucksack or Phyllis' safety glass.

Knot or not?

When the dog goes to greet his owner, which leads will knot and which will not?

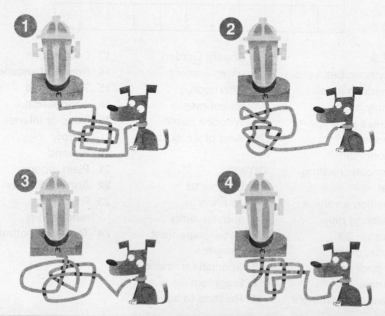

Jigsaw

Use the jigsaw pieces to recreate this completed crossword. We've only listed clues for the rows of Across words, but the pattern of the grid should help you, being symmetrical from top right to bottom left.

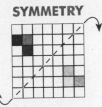

SYMMETRY

ACROSS

1. Give away treacherously
2. Settee, couch
3. Scoundrel
4. Not all
5. Medicinal quantity
6. Little mythical creature • Elapse
7. Feline
8. Cautious
9. US policeman
10. Strap of a bridle • Flow back
11. Nourish
12. Large spindle
13. Vexed, chagrined
14. Soil
15. Obey

Elimination

All but two of the listed words fall into one of the four categories. Put these leftover words together, and what word or phrase do they make?

CATEGORIES

Words following WHITE • Tools • Adjectives • Fabrics

Wrench
Gold
Saw
Sad
Moleskin
First

Spanner
Tie
House
Polyester
Tweed
Bread

Plane
Purple
Further
Dwarf
Linen
Quick

Work
Satin
Chisel
Noise

Mix-up

The clues here are all anagrams. Just unscramble the letters to get the answers. Some words have more than one anagram, so you'll need to see which fits with its neighbours.

ACROSS

1 TOPED
4 STEAD
7 TAN
8 RAW
9 LAP
10 ROOD
11 WORDY
14 STUDS
16 GNAT
18 NED
20 TAR
21 WEE
22 GREET
23 RIMES

DOWN

1 LAUD
2 OPTIONS
3 WROTE
4 HERDS
5 PAT
6 SLAYED
12 TWINERS
13 HEADER
15 TRAMS
16 MOTET
17 HARE
19 ROD

Crossword grid with numbered cells 1–23; cell 7 contains the letters A N T.

A Matter of Course

Here's a fantastic way to exercise your visual memory. Study the scene below for two minutes, paying close attention to particular elements in the scene. The grid placed over the picture should be useful – it allows you to form smaller chunks within the larger picture. Turn over to page 78 to continue the puzzle.

StepRiddle

To begin with, you can see through me.

Change my first and I'm a form, showing quality.

When my next is altered I'm really quite tactless.

Then my third gets amended to make me angry and furious.

When my fourth is changed I am birds that boast.

At the last, change my last, and I'm a mob, a horde, a host.

What was I, what did I become, and what did I turn out to be?

A Matter of Course

Can you write the number of each of these listed elements of the picture in the correct square of the grid?

1 Tyres
2 Squirrel
3 Stopwatch
4 Periscope
6 Flag
7 Cat
8 Tortoise
9 Man asleep

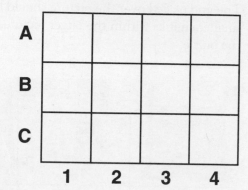

Add Up

If the number in each circle is the sum of the two below it, how quickly can you figure out the top number? You may have to work up and down the pyramid. See if you can climb the third pyramid in fewer seconds than the number you reach at the top.

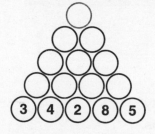

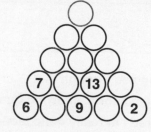

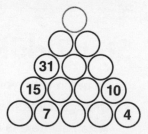

Make a list and get things done

Lists can be a great way to free your mind from the clutter of all the things you haven't done. We'd like you to write a list below of all the things that nag at you.

1 _____   6 _____

2 _____   7 _____

3 _____   8 _____

4 _____   9 _____

5 _____   10 _____

Now draw up a list of things that are easy to do – that you enjoy doing – such as relaxing in front of the television.

THINGS I LIKE DOING:

1 _____   6 _____

2 _____   7 _____

3 _____   8 _____

4 _____   9 _____

5 _____   10 _____

Write more if you like, but the point here is that whenever you're going to do something that you like doing, DO ONE SMALL THING from your annoying first list of TO-DOs. Then REWARD yourself with one of the things you like doing.

After a while, this can become a habit – you learn the habit of doing something that you ought to do before giving yourself a pat on the back (and your brain a lovely drop of rewarding dopamine!) with something you already enjoy doing.

Dilemma Fitword

Can you fit all the listed words into the two grids? You'll need to do some thinking ahead, and jumping between grids to crack this one.

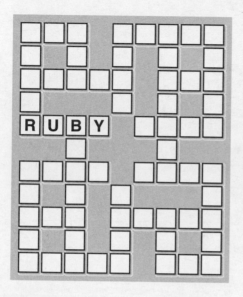 

3 Letters	HOOF	ONSET
ALL	LOBE	PITTA
GAP	OBEY	REBUS
GAS	RAZE	SEWER
ILL	ROSE	SPILL
ION	~~RUBY~~	STARK
LEA	SALT	STRAY
NEE	SELF	SUPER
NOD	THEY	~~TOPAZ~~
SKA	YANK	WALTZ
SUN		YIELD
TON	**5 Letters**	
ZEN	FATED	**7 Letters**
	FIELD	BALANCE
4 Letters	LAITY	BELIEVE
BEAK	LASER	BROWNIE
HAZY	LIEGE	SILENCE

Wheels & Cogs

When Robbie the Robot turns the handle on the cog as shown, does he discover that he needs some oil or the recharger?

Out of Hand

You'll find 22 words that can follow 'hand' to make a new word or phrase in the grid. That is, of course, if you look hard enough.

G	O	H	R	C	I	L	M	A	O	E
F	R	P	U	M	P	A	I	U	V	M
S	E	E	L	P	D	N	G	A	E	O
E	K	I	N	E	K	A	H	S	R	S
T	A	G	H	A	S	P	R	I	N	G
Z	R	N	S	C	D	T	L	V	P	M
F	B	I	S	A	R	E	A	I	M	A
B	T	T	J	A	W	E	C	N	K	I
W	U	I	C	O	B	K	K	X	D	D
O	E	R	T	A	E	L	L	A	B	E
Y	D	W	G	D	C	U	F	F	S	N

Mix & Match

You'll have to think just a little bit differently with this mixed-clue crossword. Riddles, anagrams, word association and general knowledge are all included.

ACROSS

1 CAD DEN waltzed (6)
5 Fat insect having swallowed a couple of insects, we hear (6)
8 Shock some of the best uncover (4)
9 Liberal denomination (8)
10 Word linking Body, Plated and Shining (6)
11 Connect something up in comet alert (6)
12 Parky's a master of it! (4)
14 I GOT up from warmth of duvet (3)
15 Creature's beloved, by the sound of it (4)
16 Herdsman starts to drive rams onto verdant English range (6)
18 Feature of Columba's pectorals (6)
20 From CAR NOISE a situation develops (8)
22 Word linking Baking, Cream and Water (4)
23 Anagram of TESTER (6)
24 Whole TREE IN confusion (6)

DOWN

2 Edit (5)
3 Associate with a group of musicians (7)
4 When giving out gongs, the Queen is this! (9)
5 Word coming after Keep, Match and Out (3)
6 Reach a coral island via a bridge tax (5)
7 Anagram of BLISTER (7)
11 MAIL ROGER about a pointless procedure (9)
13 Anagram of CHARITY (7)
15 Anagram of POSITED (7)
17 Road with no beginning is a place to meet (5)
19 Disturbingly, CRIED for a drink (5)
21 Is the core of truth boring? (3)

Killer Sudoku

The normal rules of Sudoku apply. Place a digit from 1-9 in each empty square so that each row, column and 3x3 block contains all the digits from 1-9. In addition, the digits in each inner shape (marked by dots) must add up to the number in the top corner of that box. No digit can be repeated within an inner shape.

Lettersets

Complete the crossword grid using the letters listed for each row and column. Cracking this one relies on anagram-solving and cross-referencing between Across and Down words.

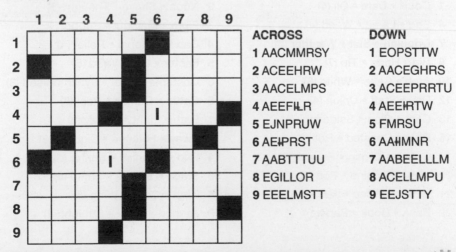

ACROSS
1 AACMMRSY
2 ACEEHRW
3 AACELMPS
4 AEEFILR
5 EJNPRUW
6 AEIPRST
7 AABTTTUU
8 EGILLOR
9 EEELMSTT

DOWN
1 EOPSTTW
2 AACEGHRS
3 ACEEPRRTU
4 AEEIRTW
5 FMRSU
6 AAHMNR
7 AABEELLLM
8 ACELLMPU
9 EEJSTTY

Missing Links

The three words in each of these clues have a fourth word in common, and that's your answer. For instance, the clue to 18 Down, 'Jagged • Knife • Straight (5)' gives you the answer EDGE (Jagged edge, Knife-edge, Straight edge).

ACROSS

1 Court • Date • Oil (4)
4 Egg • Lame • Weed (4)
7 Dripping • Suit • Weather (3)
8 Bin • Heap • Tip (7)
10 Arch • Cake • White (6)
12 Day • Staff • Union (4)
13 Cast • Clad • Soldering (4)
15 Beer • Chested • Roll (6)
19 Coffee • Organ • Pepper (7)
20 Fire • Machine • Pop (3)
21 Bended • Cap • Jerk (4)
22 Bank • Book • Paper (4)

DOWN

2 Noon • Shave • Thought (5)
3 Fibre • Majority • Support (5)
4 Bad • National • Relief (4)
5 Factor • Out • Wind (5)
6 Costume • Pool • Synchronised (8)
9 Cattle • Games • Reel (8)
11 Bath • Fight • Honey (3)
12 Away • Fetched • Sighted (3)
14 Red • Spanish • Spring (5)
16 Stage • Strings • White (5)
17 Birth • Copy • Wing (5)
18 Jagged • Knife • Straight (4)

Learn to enjoy chores

It may sound a little bit strange, perhaps even daft, but it is possible to take pleasure in peeling a potato or washing a floor. The secret lies in PAYING ATTENTION. Rather than peeling away at the potatoes thinking, 'This is tedious,' or, 'I hate peeling spuds,' pretend you're a Martian. This Martian has dropped into your brain and is seeing and feeling sights, sounds and sensations that it's never before experienced because it's undertaking a completely new activity.

If you really pay attention to something you see or do, after a while the thing you see or do loses its familiarity. Look at this word for twenty-five seconds and see what happens:

OSTRICH

Did you notice anything? Did the word start to break up or lose its familiarity? If that didn't work, try staring at a common object for a while. If you really pay attention to things, then they lose their familiarity. Importantly, when that happens they become LESS BORING: in effect, they're new. It's a bit like paying attention to your feet as you walk downstairs (and we'reNOT recommending you try it!): the act of walking downstairs can suddenly become unfamiliar because you're paying attention to it. You can get things done by making them strange, and therefore more interesting, if you use your attention in this way.

Set Square

Place one each of the digits 1-9 in each grid to make the sums work. We've put in some of the numbers to start you off. Sums should be solved from left to right, or from top to bottom.

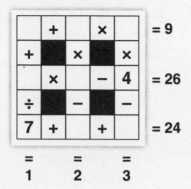

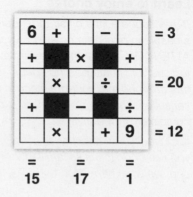

Square Eyes

Two squares in this scene are identical, though they may not be the same way up. See how quickly you can spot them.

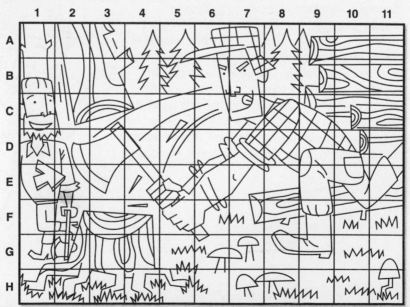

Codeword

Can you crack the code and fill in the crossword grid? Each letter of the alphabet makes at least one appearance in the grid, and is represented by the same number wherever it appears. The three letters we've decoded should help you to identify other letters and words in the grid.

13		8		2		14	10	20		8		5		25
24	13	22 C	14 O	24 D	13	24		2	4	26	25	21	13	24
2		7		13		13		10		25		2		12
17	14	4	22	25	17		6	14	10	22	2	20	21	13
13				21		14				2				10
24	13	11	2	21	10	16		22	14	18	9	7	10	13
		2		16		8		21		5		18		18
24	25	24	11		8	17	13	25	15		6	2	25	17
2		13		26		13		7		20		6		
8	26	14	2	21	13	10		8	26	21	25	16	13	24
21				25				13		14				13
14	22	22	25	8	2	14	18		25	3	14	15	13	18
24		14		17		7		25		14		2		7
5	21	25	19	2	13	10		8	1	7	25	21	2	24
13		23		22		8	25	26		17		17		13

A B C̸ O̸ E F G H I J K L M N O̸ P Q R S T U V W X Y Z

1	2	3	4	5	6	7	8	9	10	11	12	13

14	15	16	17	18	19	20	21	22	23	24	25	26
O								C		D		

Boxwise

Can you place the three-letter groups in the boxes, so that neighbouring boxes always make a six-letter word, like PAR-DON or DON-ATE? We've placed one group to start you off.

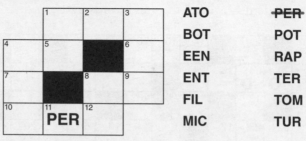

ATO	~~PER~~
BOT	POT
EEN	RAP
ENT	TER
FIL	TOM
MIC	TUR

Number Jig

All of these numbers will fit in the grid. How quickly can you get the numbers placed?

3 Digits
142
256
316
318
412
~~450~~
656
923

4 Digits
2173
2269
2472
2480
3126
3469
4169
4246
6083

9123
9410
9562

5 Digits
12786
14531
15484
20734
25587
50431
90246
95232

7 Digits
3896042
9830204

Fitword

When all of the listed words have been placed correctly in the grid, which one is left over?

3 letters
Ago
Are
Fax
Fen
Gap
Gym
Off
One
Tog
Who

4 letters
Cowl
Cusp
Dole
Hemp

Hoax
Skep
Slip
~~True~~

5 letters
Aback
Awful
Lower
Newer
Nifty
Spoof

6 letters
Parted
Phoned

Do you find it hard to concentrate?

We've six questions for you to answer. Circle the number by the response that best fits how you feel. When you've answered all the questions, add up the numbers and go to page 94.

- *Do you ever start reading an instruction manual for something new and find your attention has drifted before you've taken in the information?*   * A lot 2   Sometimes 1   Hardly ever 0
- *Have your eyes ever moved over an article or book without your mind taking in what you've been reading?*   * A lot 2   Sometimes 1   Hardly ever 0
- *Listening to the weather forecast, does your mind wander before the forecast gets to your region?*   * A lot 2   Sometimes 1   Hardly ever 0
- *On being introduced to somebody, do you find that you can't recall their name just seconds later?*   * A lot 2   Sometimes 1   Hardly ever 0
- *Do you find that you tend not to finish tasks because you lose concentration?*
- *Do you find that you tend to make mistakes because you haven't been concentrating properly?*

Sudoku

Place a number in each empty square so that each row, each column and each 2x2 block contains all the numbers from 1-4.

		1	
			4
2			
3	4		

2			3
	4	1	

			3
		4	
	3	2	
2			

Logical

Try solving this little logical problem in your head before putting pen to paper.

Three student friends had lined up jobs at the Midsummer Magic music festivals around the country. Christine's job wasn't in Leeds, and nor was it as a chef. Penny – not the waitress – would be working in London, while the steward, who wasn't Jo, would be working in Liverpool.

Who had which job where?

Jigsaw

How quickly can you figure out what's what?
Use the jigsaw pieces to recreate this completed
crossword. We've only listed clues for the rows of
Across words, but the pattern of the grid should
help you, being symmetrical from top right to
bottom left.

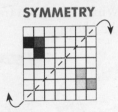

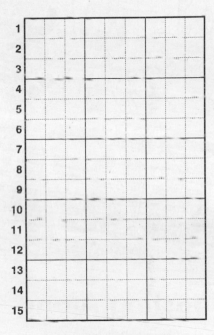

ACROSS

1 Doctor for animals
2 Passenger-carrying car • Leave out
3 Half a dozen
4 Chair, eg • Coloured part of the eye
5 Boogie, bop
6 Sailors' drink • Small green vegetable
7 Bury

8 Measurement of land • Confidential assistant
9 Conscious
10 Half a barrel • Compete
11 Lax
12 Ship's team of workers • Prepare material for publication
13 Forthwith, immediately
14 On a former occasion • Wide-mouthed pitcher
15 Fisherman's long stick with a reel

For Arms

Which of the ten transfers produces the temporary tattoo shown on the forearm?

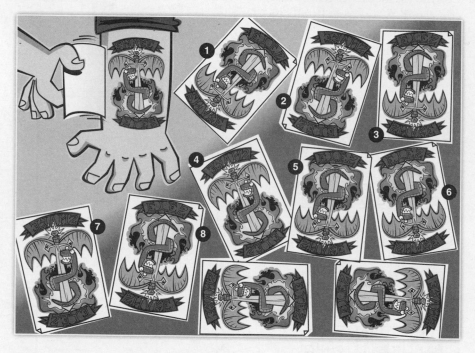

Coasting Along

Ah, the Great British seaside, don't you just love it? There are fifteen seaside towns from the UK to find in the grid. Have fun on your travels!

B	R	E	M	O	R	C	S	A
O	L	T	D	R	N	D	C	Y
N	E	A	M	Y	U	G	A	T
D	H	G	C	N	R	S	R	E
U	S	R	B	K	E	O	B	L
D	U	A	R	H	P	O	O	S
N	R	M	T	H	B	O	R	I
A	T	O	T	A	Y	T	O	L
L	R	U	N	C	D	L	U	L
L	O	N	A	I	R	N	G	I
S	P	L	A	R	G	S	H	M

Mix & Match

This mixed-clue crossword will get you thinking in lots of different ways. Riddles, anagrams, word association and general knowledge are all included.

ACROSS

1 Decline with student's misery (8)
5 Master cook (4)
9 Such essential signs show life (5)
10 Sticky tarry substance used in road-building (7)
11 Bird which left Noah's boat? (4)
12 EU country, capital Sofia (8)
14 Vote on the fourteenth letter and it might make you sneeze (6)
15 Affectionate name for the monster said to live in a large Scottish lake (6)
18 Tenant evolves to CUT CAPON (8)
20 Flowing rock? (4)
23 Imitation drug put with smelly problem! (7)
24 Plot surprise for Dickens' Oliver (5)
25 Word following Guy, Tight and Tow (4)
26 ___ Boy, Cliff Richard song (8)

DOWN

1 Word coming before Rest, Crossing and Headed (5)
2 Tone that is neither sharp nor flat (7)
3 Description of US TV's Betty (4)
4 Overcome when payment comes around (6)
6 Cartoon Simpson's a poet (5)
7 Supporter's food makes a trumpet flourish (7)
8 GETS RAG to somehow make reel (7)
13 Anagram of STEEPED (4-3)
14 This means of getting rich isn't for cheats! (7)
16 King Charles' cocker! (7)
17 Discover some orang or a goat (6)
19 Writers and athletes can get this pain (5)
21 Anagram of LATER (5)
22 Long for a bit of chit-chat (4)

How did you score?

9 –12 You find it quite hard to concentrate across a lot of different activities. Perhaps you've always been like this – some people are. But if this is a sudden change, it would be worth just chatting to your doctor about it. If you've always had poor concentration, read on for some tips and exercises.

5 – 8 You have some problems with concentration in certain areas of your life. If these are mainly in reading, it may mean that you're not a great reader – it's harder to concentrate on things we find more difficult. On the other hand, it may mean simply that you need to practise a bit more to aid your concentration.

0 – 4 You don't have too much of a problem concentrating, but some of the tips I'm providing this time may help you fine-tune your concentration a little more.

Now turn to page 98.

Futoshiki

Fill the blank squares so that each row and column contains all the numbers 1, 2 and 3 in the smaller grids, and 1, 2, 3 and 4 in the larger grid. Use the given numbers and the symbols that tell you if the number in the square is larger (>) or smaller (<) than the number next to it.

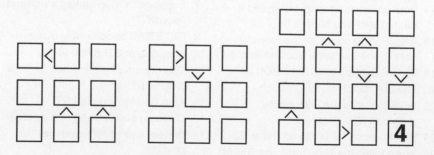

Dateline

Work out the answers to the clues to discover the date in the shaded space – a significant date in English history (and for English literature!). Calculators strictly forbidden!

ACROSS

1 Days In 3 weeks x months in a year
4 12 x 12 x 6
6 2 Down + 22 Across
8 104 x 8
9 2516 doubled
11 Baker's dozen + 1
12 Square root of 556, or hours in a day
13 Mystery date
16 11 Down – 3 Down
17 Cube root of 1331
19 Anagram of 14 Down
21 Double 16 Across
22 34,567 + 24,295
24 24 x 6 + 235
25 113 x 7

DOWN

1 5005 – 3333 + 509
2 7007 x 4 + 174
3 Half a century
4 8 Across + 8
5 6263 – 1234 – 205
7 1 Down x players in a trio
10 11 Down + 13 Down
11 5% of 2220
13 6 cubed
14 10,010 – 3832
15 23,228 + 23,418 + 23,481
16 18,369 ÷ 3
18 111,111 ÷ 3 ÷ 7
20 Half of 1718
23 Number of pages, including the covers, of *Puzzler Brain Pad* minus 110

Codeword

Can you crack the code and fill in the crossword grid? Each letter of the alphabet makes at least one appearance in the grid, and is represented by the same number wherever it appears. The five letters we've decoded should help you to identify other letters and words in the grid.

24		14		18		24	9	3		16		18		20
22	15	11	3	19	21	18		19	25	15	19	5	3	10
6		15		25		5		25		19		15		16 **W**
3	7	13	12	17	4		19	17	19	5	24	21	17	17 **O**
10			12		12				3					11 **R**
21	17	11	10	24	22	17		24	21	21	11	24	19	21 **T**
	20		11		21		23		18		14			25 **H**
1	24	7	2		23	15	12	12	4		16	15	12	4
17		2		14		17		17		3		12		
19	12	24	11	15	17	10		24	20	18	21	3	11	3
5				26			21		8					9
3	7	2	3	26	26	12	3		8	20	3	10	19	25
4		17		24		24		24		15		3		24
3	13	15	14	11	24	7		13	25	11	24	18	24	12
22		12		22		2	3	21		3		21		3

A B C D E F G H̷ I J K L M N Ø P Q R̷ S T̷ U V W̷ X Y Z

1	2	3	4	5	6	7	8	9	10	11 **R**	12	13
14	15	16 **W**	17 **O**	18	19	20	21 **T**	22	23	24	25 **H**	26

TIP

Your codeword-solving skills rely on the size of your vocabulary. This time, once you've filled in all the starter letters in the grid, you should be able to deduce the word reading across and ending on the letter O. Filling in the discovered letters from here should then lead you to finding the first word on the sixth row, and so on.

Arroword

Just follow the arrows to write your answers in the grid. A handful of anagram clues will get you thinking differently.

Words of wisdom	▼	Bible's first woman	▼	Drifted on the surface	▼	Firearm		▼	SLENDER (anagram)	SISTER (anagram)
Make known (a secret) ►						▼			Large stringed instrument	
Teapot top		WARD (anagram)		Small measure of weight ►				▼		
►		▼	Thurman, *Kill Bill* actress	South American mountains ►						
TRUCE (anagram)			▼			Old Testament priest ►				
				LASER (anagram) ►						
Ray of light	DAWN (anagram)					Heavy drinker ►				

StepRiddle

Before I'm changed, I'm over-loud for your hearing.

Change my first to discover a graceful bearing.

My second is changed and I force open with a lever.

Change my next and I'm writing with no rhyme scheme or metre.

Change my fourth, then I'm liable to be lying flat.

At the last, change my last and you'll see me sticking out.

What was I, what did I become, and what did I turn out to be?

Everyone loses concentration

Concentration is hard. No-one can sit through a talk or lecture and take everything in, and we all struggle when reading through complicated jargon-filled instructions for a new piece of technology.

Here's the first fact about concentration: **our brains find it hard to concentrate**. *Our brains have evolved quite naturally to notice important things such as food and danger: when something is threatening us, or when there's tasty food before our eyes, we concentrate effortlessly.*

The second fact about concentration is that **our brains are hungry for change and novelty**. *Think about the world of advertising – we're encouraged to concentrate on products by the use of strange situations, flashing lights, changing colours and loud catchy music.*

So, it's quite natural that our attention can drift when reading the small print on an insurance document, or the notes from an evening class for example – there isn't any novelty in these situations. Nevertheless it is really important to know what you're getting into. Turn the page and I'll start to explain how you can help your brain to learn to do such difficult tasks.

Staircase

When these politics terms are correctly fitted in the rows of the grid, another such term will appear down the diagonal staircase.

BUDGET
CABAL
CHARTER
CLAUSE
EDICT
JUNTA
MANDATE

Training the puppy called Attention

Learning to concentrate is a bit like training a puppy. Now, that may sound a bit strange, but think about it. We've already discovered that concentration revolves around paying attention, and that attention wanders quite naturally, always on the look-out for something new – exactly like a puppy that doesn't do what it's told.

Now, if you think about how you train a puppy, the key is to find some small thing that they can do properly, and then to provide a reward immediately. It doesn't matter what the reward is – a biscuit, a pat, a cuddle or saying, 'good boy!' What matters is that the reward is provided straightaway: you'd be waiting all day if you held back with the reward until good behaviour lasted for reasonably long periods of time. Rather, when training a puppy you begin by rewarding them for what they can (sometimes!) do already.

That's exactly what you need to do with concentration.

You'll find the first part of our training regime on page 127.

Mind the Gap

Can you place a well-known three-letter word in the spaces of each row to complete the seven-letter word? Do it correctly, and the shaded letters should spell out something associated with jewellery.

H	I	C				S
P	O	P				S
R	E				A	L
P	L				E	R
I	M				C	H
P	U	D				G
P	O	S				E

Pathfinder

Beginning with SAILING, and moving up, down, left or right, one letter at a time, can you trace a path of fifteen Olympic sports?

G	N	I	R	G	N	I	T	I	E	W
W	R	W	O	A	N	I	F	G	E	Y
S	E	S	N	H	D	L	T	H	K	C
T	I	A	O	L	B	A	L	L	H	O
L	L	G	T	H	T	I	C	S	O	O
I	I	N	R	I	A	T	E	S	H	T
N	G	B	A	A	T	H	L	L	E	I
I	D	T	L	L	O	V	O	L	Y	N
V	O	F	O	T	D	U	J	L	B	G
I	S	F	O	B	A	L	L	L	A	G
N	G	S	C	I	T	S	A	N	M	Y

Sudoku

Use your powers of reasoning to place numbers in the grid, so that each row, each column and each 3x3 block contains the numbers 1-9.

		2	8	6			7	5
		5	4			6		
3	7				9	8		
2	1			7	5			
7			2		3	1		
		3	1	9	4			
	2	8		4		9	3	1
9						2	5	
6						7		

Lose a Letter

Cross out one letter in each square to leave a completed crossword. You may have to think ahead to rule out some red herrings along the way.

B/T	A/U	B/S	▨	E/W	A/E	C/S	H/L	A/I	I/N	E/G
H/L	▨	P/R	R	A/O	▨	L/O	▨	M/R	▨	N/O
O/U	D/N	I/O	F/U	X/Y	▨	S/U	P/U	E/P	E/S	R/S
M/R	▨	B/N	▨	▨	▨	R/T	▨	▨	▨	E/U
B/N	E/U	E/N	C/G	I/L	E/N	G/R	▨	G/H	A/U	D/E
▨	▨	E/R	▨	N/O	▨	E/U	▨	A/O	▨	▨
C/P	O/U	S/Y	▨	C/S	I/U	D/T	D/E	L/O	E/W	D/N
A/E	▨	▨	▨	I/K	▨	▨	▨	L/P	▨	A/E
M/T	A/O	C/L	E/H	O/S	S	▨	A/C	B/L	A/E	F/L/I/T
A/E	▨	I/O	▨	T/U	U	▨	A/P	▨	G/O	E/V
A/L	O/S	B/T	S/U	E/T	E/O	R/S	▨	E/N	O/Y	E/R

Pic and Mix

From the pictures and comments below, can you match the student to their contribution to the picnic?

ANDRÉ: I didn't bring something with 4 corners.

GEORGE: I brought something savoury.

KEIKO: No comment.

TANITA: I made something typically British.

SAMOSAS: I was brought by a woman.

SANDWICHES: No comment.

SCONES: No comment.

SHORTBREAD: No comment.

Word Builder

Using the nine letters provided, can you answer these clues? Every answer must include the highlighted letter P. Which man-made fabric uses all nine letters?

T	R	Y
O	P	E
L	E	S

5 Letters
Ward off, drive back
Run off to marry
Answer
Incline
Stares
Fit of temper
Non-verse writing

6 Letters
Rest
Torment, harass
Tired
Car fuel
Sea eagle
Rotund
Billboard ad

7 Letters
Keys in again
Skin disease
Sharply, exorbitantly

Missing Links _____

The three words in each of these clues have a fourth word in common, and that's your answer. For instance, the clue to 2 Down, 'Burst • Print • Side (3)' gives you the answer OUT (Outburst, Printout, Outside).

1		2 O		3	■	4		5	■	6
	■	U	■	■	■	■	■	■	■	
7		T			■	■	8			
	■	■	■		■		■		■	
9		10		■	11				■	12
	■	■		■		■	■	■	■	
■		13	14		15			■		
16			■		■	■		■	■	
17			■	18			■	19		
	■	■	■		■		■		■	
20				■	21					

ACROSS

1 Pop • Reading • Therapy (5)
4 Fairy • Tall • Tell (5)
7 Measures • Sports • Unction (7)
8 Cotton • Pink • Rummy (3)
9 Bank • Mission • Under (9)
13 *Beret* • Jam • Ripple (9)
17 Faced • Time • Tone (3)
18 Day • Participle • Value (7)
20 Andre • *Blue* • Kay (5)
21 Boat • Day • Pipe (5)

DOWN

1 Elbow • Monkey • Paint (6)
2 Burst • Print • Side (3)
3 Chess • Meal • Party (5)
4 Fore • Upon • With (5)
5 Cigarette • Fire • High (7)
6 Bird • Plain • Swan (4)
10 Heathrow • Lounge • Terminal (7)
11 Reference • Relief • Weather (3)
12 Computer • Nervous • Solar (6)
14 Market • Model • Power (5)
15 Garlic • Roll • Sauce (5)
16 Bus • Cock • Full (4)
19 Lash • Naked • Sore (3)

Backwords

The answers to this crossword are all here, along with extra letters where the black squares should be. Can you black out any unwanted letters to leave a grid that matches the clues (which are out of order)? The finished grid will have full symmetry.

I	M	P	F	A	M	E	D	U	P	E
B	E	A	U	S	E	F	U	N	I	T
I	M	U	S	T	A	F	F	C	E	U
S	O	L	E	I	S	O	F	O	R	T
A	D	E	V	O	U	R	A	M	E	O
C	O	M	P	A	R	T	M	E	N	T
K	N	U	A	T	E	P	E	G	O	A
S	U	R	F	A	M	E	H	A	I	L
E	P	A	O	P	E	R	A	I	N	Y
T	O	F	U	E	N	A	Z	O	N	E
A	N	T	R	A	T	T	Y	A	S	H

ACROSS

- Musical drama
- Military stronghold
- Ride a wave
- Male sweetheart
- Celebrated
- Rod, baton
- Fish, either Lemon or Dover
- Greet exaltedly
- Soya bean curd
- Train carriage section
- Bad-tempered
- Single entity
- Area

DOWN

- Size, dimension
- Atop
- Complete
- Written reminder
- Large mailbags
- Join by melting
- Last Greek character
- Indistinct
- Monkey-like mammal
- Number of sides of a parallelogram
- Taverns
- Of poor quality
- Large jetty

Picture Pair

How quickly can you spot the two identical pictures?

Six Pack

Can you place digits in the empty triangles, so that the numbers in each hexagon add up to 25? Only single digits between 1 and 9 can be used, and no two numbers in any hexagon may be the same.

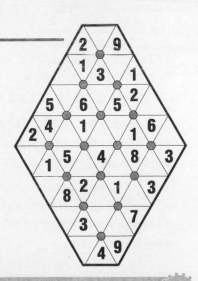

Drop Quote

Here's a quotation from Alfred Hitchcock about television. The words have dropped out of position into the columns below. Can you restore the quote?

		MURDER			CAN
	WORK			ANTAGONISMS.	
IF				,	
		GIVE			.

COMMERCIALS	YOU	HAVEN'T	ANY	SOME	AND
~~IF~~	WILL	~~GIVE~~	ONE'S	ANTAGONISMS	THE
HELP	~~WORK~~	OFF	ON	~~ANTAGONISMS~~	~~CAN~~
SEEING	A	~~MURDER~~	YOU	TELEVISION	

Mobile Quotes

We've put three quotations in code, using the numbers on a mobile keypad. So, for instance, the first letter of the first quote could be D, E or F. Can you work out what Jimmy Connors said?

"3973743623 47 2 47328 238268243. 843
7762536 47 8428 9436 968 438 843 3973743623,
968'73 866 326633 653 86 873 48."

"639 9675377 5683 48 9436 968 77455 9687
4887 688 84373. 77455 9687 4887 28 946253366
263 8439 6253 968 7867 263 25326 48 87."

"728437 8426 8439464 2 27433 7352773 2225
86 4622848489 27 2 3245873, 87328 48 27 2
242553643 263 879 86 438 2225 66 87225 27
7666 27 76774253."

1	2 ABC	3 DEF
4 GHI	5 JKL	6 MNO
7 PQRS	8 TUV	9 WXYZ
*	0	#

Dilemma Crossword

The clues for these crosswords have been mixed up. As you solve them, you'll need to work out which answer goes in each grid.

ACROSS

1 Get rid of • Analysis and judgement of a work of art

7 Keyboard instrument with pipes • Fish-eating riverbank animal

8 Domain, kingdom • Rich part of milk

10 Slippery creatures • Flower with a tiger variety

11 Car's impact absorber • Recites

14 Ennui • Talkative bird

15 Rabbit-like animal • Gathered facts

17 Popular Italian dish • Channels of information

19 Had, possessed • Make changes to

20 Polite • Golden dog breed

DOWN

2 Steady, uniform • Shaken, upset

3 Quality of sound • Pub-game arrow

4 Prickly desert plant • Travelling entertainment show

5 Expanse of salt water • Secure with a knot

6 Drive, impetus • Round sweet on a stick

9 Deceives, sends astray • Mythical damsels with tails

12 Raised flat piece of land • Learner

13 Luxurious variety of wool • Foreign nanny (2,4)

16 Gap • Gateau

18 Menagerie • Female rabbit

Sudoku

Use your powers of reasoning to place numbers in the grid, so that each row, each column and each 3x3 block contains the numbers 1-9.

	2					9		
8		4			5	1		
	3					6		8
				6		3		7
			2				8	1
	8				7	4		
9	4	6	3		8	7		
				5				9
		5	6	1			3	

Alpha-Beater

Every letter of the alphabet has been removed from this crossword once. How quickly can you put all 26 back? Use the A-Z list to cross off letters as you use them.

O				A				D	
G	L	A	N			U		I	P
		T		O		D			
E		M		T			L	A	
		A		T		A		E	
A		U	A		B		E		T
	U								
M		N	I	A		E	X	A	
	D			T		Y			U

A	B	C	D	E	F	G	H	I	J	K	L	M
N	O	P	Q	R	S	T	U	V	W	X	Y	Z

Set Square

Place one each of the digits 1-9 in each grid to make the sums work. We've put in some of the numbers to start you off. Sums should be solved from left to right, or from top to bottom.

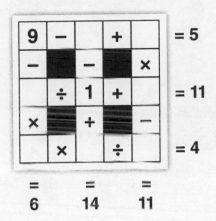

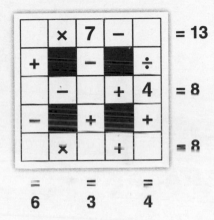

Elimination

All but two of the listed words fall into one of the four categories. Put these leftover words together, and what word or phrase do they make?

CATEGORIES

Furniture • Words meaning TWINE • Yellow things • Items associated with Scotland

Rope	Cord	Thread	Whisky
Daffodil	Yarn	Wardrobe	String
Haggis	Kilt	Ball	Chair
Divan	Lemon	Bagpipes	Canary
Table	Shortbread	Dresser	
Room	Banana	Yolk	

Kim's Game

Ready for a memory challenge? Study these athletes for 30 seconds, then turn the page.

Fairy Good Show

Your local village hall is the venue for a production of *A Midsummer Night's Dream*. Here's a list of the cast who have roles as fairies, and the roles they play. Study the list for two minutes, then turn to page 115. Try to concentrate on the surnames and character names.

A Midsummer Night's Dream - Cast:

Andy Hopkins	Oberon
Celia Inman	Titania
Davina Michaels	Puck
Joe Smith	Peaseblossom
Oliver Lawrence	Cobweb
Penny Wilson	Moth
Rob McLeod	Mustardseed

Kim's Game

See page 110 before having a go at these questions. Looking at the sports on this page, can you tell what has changed from the previous page?

1 Which two original athletes have been removed?
2 Which two new athletes have been added?
3 What other three changes have been made to the pictures?

Making a Splash

There are thirteen things linked with swimming to find in the grid. Perfect for our rainy summers.

G	S	K	N	U	R	T	Y	Y
F	E	D	J	C	L	R	L	G
M	L	L	N	O	R	F	F	C
E	G	I	O	A	R	A	O	T
D	G	P	P	E	B	S	W	S
L	O	O	T	P	T	M	N	L
E	G	T	X	U	E	O	R	A
Y	U	W	M	P	R	R	D	A
B	A	E	S	K	V	B	S	H
L	I	F	E	G	U	A	R	D
K	U	L	B	I	K	I	N	I

Three to One

You'll have to think ahead to complete this crossword. You have a choice of three words to put in each space, but which will fit with its neighbours?

	1	2		3		4		5	
6									
7				8					9
10			11			12			
13 O	N 14	L	Y		15	16		17	
			18						
19							20		
	21				22				

ACROSS

1 Scam • Scan • Scar
4 Bevy • Hive • Tear
7 Emu • Era • Eye
8 Bellhop • Midship • Milksop
10 Eighty • Eyelet • Tahiti
12 Bran • Brig • Brow
13 Ogre • Once • Only
15 Fleece • Plasma • Sherpa
19 Fiancée • Flasher • Flushed
20 One • Owl • Own
21 Dyes • Lyre • Step
22 Earn • Nose • Nuts

DOWN

2 Cheer • Clang • Crush
3 Mount • Names • Remit
4 Bide • Dill • Hulk
5 Abhor • Visor • Voter
6 Beetroot • Generous • Werewolf
9 Pertains • Pigtails • Powdered
11 Hay • Hoe • Icy
12 Big • Boa • Ova
14 Carry • Lousy • Roast
16 Hedge • Hurry • Laden
17 Epoch • Roots • Shout
18 Acts • Shoe • Whet

Kakuro

Simple addition and a bit of logical thinking will solve this one. You must write a digit in each white square so that the digits in each block add up to the total in the box above or to the left. 1-9 are the only digits to use and, although you may find a digit repeated in a row, it must not be repeated in the same block. We've solved one block for you.

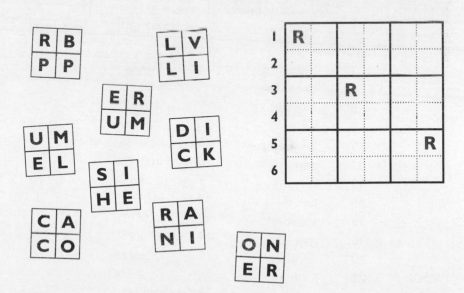

Mini Jigsaw

Fit the pieces in the grid to spell out a chemical element in each row.

First Thoughts

Fill in the blank in each clue to make a well-known word or phrase, then write your answers in the grid. We've solved one clue to start you off.

ACROSS

1 ___ Kidman (6)
4 ___ beetle (4)
8 ___ bag (3)
9 ___ Falls (7)
10 ___ taking (5)
11 ___ page (5)
13 ___ dog (5)
15 ___ fish (5)
17 ___ steak (7)
19 ___ nap (3)
20 ___ wise (4)
21 ___ Club (6)

DOWN

1 ___ Peace Prize (5)
2 ___ lens (7)
3 ___ corporal (5)
5 ___ cake (3)
6 ___ fruit (5)
7 ___ horse (4)
12 ___ tart (7)
13 ___ land (5)
14 ___ wink (4)
15 ___ Claus (5)
16 ___ America (5)
18 ___ doll (3)

Memory Quiz

Here's a quiz to see how much attention you're really paying to your surroundings. No peeping!

1 What, apart from white, is the colour of the Oxfam logo?

2 Which is the correct spelling – presede, preseed, preceed or precede?

3 How many sections are on the 'Wheel of Health' labelling system used by most supermarkets?

4 In which month of 2007 did Gordon Brown become prime minister?

5 What was significant about the year Virginia Wade became the last British Wimbledon champion?

6 Which brand of washing-up liquid includes a baby on its logo?

7 In the TV series, what colour was Inspector Morse's Jaguar?

8 How many ducks did Hilda Ogden's 'muriel' have in *Coronation Street*?

Fairy Good Show

See if you can complete the cast list from page 110.

A Midsummer Night's Dream - Cast:

Andy _____   _____
Celia _____   _____
Davina _____   _____
Joe _____   _____
Oliver _____   _____
Penny _____   _____
Rob _____   _____

Court Out

I'm not sure I've ever been in a court, but I know that some people go and watch trials as entertainment! There are fourteen things you might find in a court listed, and your challenge here is to fit them into the grid.

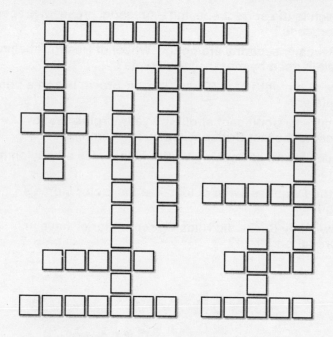

3 letters
WIG

4 letters
DOCK
GOWN

5 letters
BENCH
CLERK
COURT
TRIAL

7 letters
ACCUSED
BAILIFF

9 letters
BARRISTER
SOLICITOR
VIDEO LINK

10 letters
COAT OF ARMS
MAGISTRATE

Futoshiki

Fill the blank squares so that each row and column contains all the numbers 1, 2 and 3 in the smaller grids, and 1, 2, 3 and 4 in the larger grid. Use the given numbers and the symbols that tell you if the number in the square is larger (>) or smaller (<) than the number next to it.

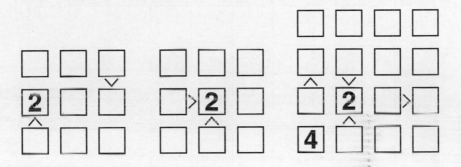

Sudoku

Use your powers of reasoning to place numbers in the grid, so that each row, each column and each 3x3 block contains the numbers 1-9.

4	2							8
				6			7	
3			5	8		9		
			4	5		2	8	
6					7			
			6	3		1	4	
9			3	1		8		
				4			3	
8		5						9

Arroword

Just follow the arrows to write your answers in the grid. Are the anagram clues a help or hindrance?

Vessel used on canals	Girl in Wonderland	PLATTER (anagram)		Possess		Ocean traveller		And so on (abbr)	
LISTS (anagram)		RAIL (anagram)		Style of window		Fizzy water		Word-based jokes	
COAGULATE (anagram)				Moisture of a tree				Hole of a needle	
				Refuse to admit					
LIVES (anagram)	Practise on stage								

Word Sleuth

Use your powers of deduction to work out our four-letter mystery word. The four different letters in the mystery word can be worked out by comparing the scores of the clue words. Every letter in a clue word that is in the mystery word is scored with a circle, black if the letter is in the correct place, grey if it isn't. So, for example, TRAM shares three letters with our mystery word, but only one of them is in the correct position.

Go to page 120 for a starter hint.

CLUE WORD	Score
T R A M	● ● ●
A R M Y	● ●
A N T E	● ●
S T E W	● ●
N E A R	● ●
M A S T	● ● ●

MYSTERY WORD

● ● ● ●

Droid Rage

Which of the twelve chips does the Droid need to repair the computer board?

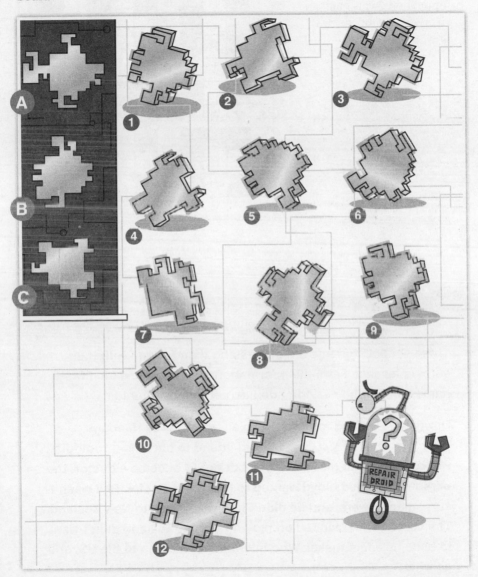

Vowel Play

Do you recognise all these words without their vowels? Just put the vowels back correctly to complete the crossword.

PAGE 118 WORD SLEUTH HINT

Compare TRAM and MAST and you can deduce the correct position of one letter, and another letter which isn't in its correct position.

P		Q				N		N	T	H
				N						
V				J		R			R	
		R				T				V
	S	T		Y		H		S	T	
								T		N
S	Y	R		P		V			D	
T								F		S
	L	K		K		T		F		P
										R
M		Y		R		R		N	N	Y

Logical

Try solving this logical problem in your head before putting pen to paper.

Three school students are discussing their futures with their careers teacher. From the information given below, match first names and surnames, intended career and destination.

Dawn, who wanted to emigrate to a Commonwealth country, wasn't surnamed McGrath but did intend to become a zoologist. Robbie wanted to move to India, but not to become a doctor: the person surnamed Lloyd wanted to become a doctor. Phil wasn't surnamed Powers, and he didn't intend to move to New Zealand. The person who planned on moving to New Zealand didn't want to become a film-maker. Who intended on moving to the US, and as what?

Skeleton

Despite appearances, this is a regular crossword, symmetrical from top right to bottom left. So the small amount of information we've given (numbers and black squares) will help a great deal in filling in the full grid pattern.

SYMMETRY

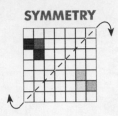

ACROSS

- **1** Stand in, proxy
- **4** Trace of a wound
- **8** OT song
- **9** Shrimp-like creature
- **10** Captivate
- **13** Throw light on
- **15** Pertaining to an Indian religion
- **16** Clichéd
- **18** Roofing slate
- **19** High-pitched cry

DOWN

- **1** Topple, overthrow
- **2** *The Princess and the ___*, fairy story
- **3** Noisy and disorderly
- **5** ___ Schiffer, supermodel
- **6** Skating surface
- **7** Positive
- **11** Undying
- **12** Save (someone)
- **14** Close
- **17** Extreme annoyance

Knot or not?

When the bomb disposal expert pulls on the fuses, which will knot and which will not?

Jigsaw

Use the jigsaw pieces to recreate this completed crossword. We've only listed clues for the rows of Across words, but the pattern of the grid should help you, being symmetrical from top right to bottom left.

SYMMETRY

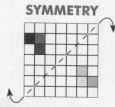

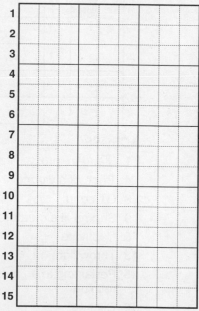

L	A	R		S	E	D		M		G	I			E	D
		N		A		O		A			E			L	L
	P			G	H	T		M	O	T		S	S	E		L	A

E	P		E		O		C	E	L		G	E	S		I		O
	I	N		E	M	U		H		E			A		D	W	E
E	L			D		R		O	W	N		N	K	Y		O	

C	C	U			E		C	O	R		I		A		S	T	E
O				E	R	T		U		U		B	U	D			R
M	I		E			A		B	L	E		I		Z		H	A	Z

ACROSS

1 Formally charged

2 Plant shoot

3 Physical strength

4 Immerse

5 Lifeless, passive

6 Light-brown nut

7 Room for wine?

9 US soul and R&B record label

10 Borders, rims

11 Live, reside

12 Tall and ungainly

13 Welsh breed of dog

14 Australian bird

15 Sanctified

Pattern Maker

If a dotted line indicates a cut, and an uninterrupted line indicates a fold, which of the five patterns is produced when you fold and cut the square of paper as indicated?

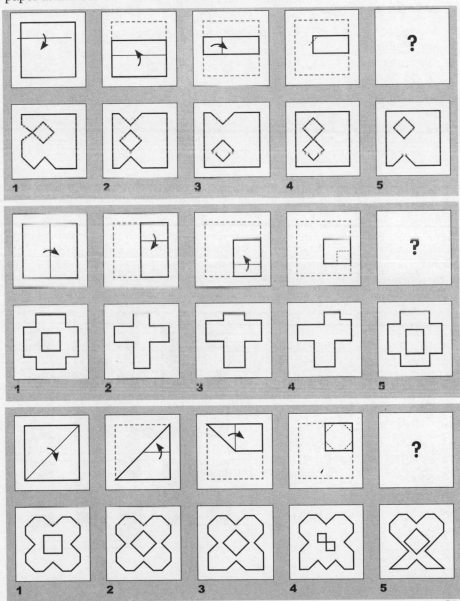

Elimination

All but two of the listed words fall into one of the four categories. Put these leftover words together, and what word or phrase do they make?

CATEGORIES

Words preceding BABY • Church features • Flowers • Words associated with 'Piano'

Cry	Altar	Iris	Test-tube
Bolt	Crocus	Stool	Tulip
Nave	War	Aisle	Apse
Rose	Jelly	Hyacinth	Tuner
Bush	Key	Upright	
Grand	Thunder	Font	

Mix-up

The clues here are all anagrams. Just unscramble the letters to get the answers. Some words have more than one anagram, so you'll need to see which fits with its neighbours.

ACROSS
1 RECAP
4 ROODS
7 OWE
8 WAS
9 ALE
10 TUNS
11 HEART
14 LASER
16 SPAN
18 DAP
20 WEE
21 DOE
22 WROTE
23 MOANS

DOWN
1 WASP
2 HECTARE
3 SIREN
4 SOWED
5 LOW
6 WHEATS
12 SENORAS
13 POSTED
15 REAMS
16 TAMES
17 AMEN
19 WED

Forefully Good

Here's a fantastic way to exercise your visual memory. Study the scene below for two minutes, paying close attention to particular elements in the scene. The grid placed over the picture should be useful – it allows you to form smaller chunks within the larger picture.

Turn over to page 126 to continue the puzzle.

Forefully Good

Can you write the number of each of these listed elements of the picture in the correct square of the grid?

1 Rake
2 Sparrow
3 Pink cap
4 Moustache
5 Squirrel
6 Rabbit
7 Striped jumper
8 Red golf bag
9 Duck
10 Pink plus-fours

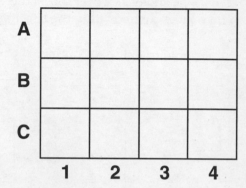

Add Up

If the number in each circle is the sum of the two below it, how quickly can you figure out the top number? You may have to work up and down the pyramid. See if you can climb the third pyramid in fewer seconds than the number you reach at the top.

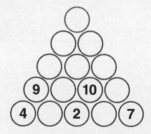
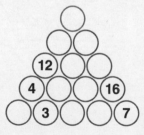

Concentration in the ebb and flow of life

We've concentrated (excuse the pun!) on reading so far, but we all know that concentration isn't just a problem when reading. Have you ever noticed when driving, for example, that you've no memory whatsoever of the last few minutes, that your mind has been elsewhere and you've been driving without consciously paying attention – without concentration?

This can happen in all sorts of situations, even when sitting chatting to family and friends. Now, sometimes you may well want to have your mind elsewhere on such occasions, but at other times this may result in regrets, problems or even mistakes. So how do we deal with this? Well, always remember that you can help to bring your mind into what you're doing, and therefore you can help yourself to better your concentration. Here's how:

Spend five minutes in a quiet place, sitting quietly and breathing in and out slowly and comfortably. Imagine you're training our puppy, attention, by taking it for a walk back and forth with your breath. As you breathe, your breath moves from the middle of your chest up to the top of your head. Then it goes back down, and so on. Imagine the puppy – your attention – has to learn to follow the breath up and down as part of its training. This is the first element of your concentration training – learn to follow your breath with your attention, up and down.

Don't panic if your attention drifts – It will! All of a sudden, you'll be aware that you're thinking of something else and that your puppy has wandered off. Don't worry, though – just noticing that your attention has strayed is an important part of the training. All you need to do is gently pull your attention back to the path of the breath, as you would a puppy.

In summary, a good way of training your concentration (though not while behind the wheel of a car, of course), is to:

A Follow your breath going up and down with your attention.
B Learn to notice when your attention – as it will – drifts away to another thought or sensation.
C Gently bring it back to your breath. If this were a puppy, you would have to do this hundreds of times before it learned to follow without running off. The same is true for your attention – you have to let it run off and gently pull it back hundreds of times before it will learn to do this itself.

You'll find my final thoughts this time on page 134.

Dilemma Fitword

Can you fit all the listed words into the two grids? You'll need to do some thinking ahead, and jumping between grids to crack this one.

3 Letters	4 Letters	5 Letters	PLEAD
ASH	ACID	APHID	PLUMB
BUS	AIRY	BURKA	SALAD
BUY	ATOP	COYPU	SCRAP
EAR	DROP	DIRGE	
HIP	DUPE	EXTRA	7 Letters
OAR	FATE	FLOAT	HATCHET
PUB	FIRE	FRAIL	HOTFOOT
SAY	FREE	LASER	PARLOUR
TOP	ROLE	LAYER	PITCHER
TOR	~~SHOE~~	LURID	
YAP	~~SHOP~~	OTHER	
YES	STUB	PAPER	

Wheels & Cogs

When Hambo the hamster runs as shown, will the pointer turn to ball 1 or ball 2?

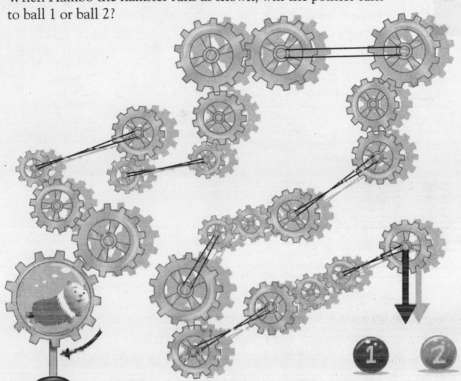

Sock 'n' Sole

You should be able to find seventeen different types of footwear in the grid, without it turning into too much of a footslog!

S	K	P	H	I	G	H	H	E	E	L
N	L	L	L	P	M	U	P	S	P	P
E	E	I	Q	A	O	U	P	S	O	R
A	U	M	N	X	D	A	L	L	T	E
K	G	S	F	G	D	N	F	E	T	N
E	O	O	R	R	B	P	A	G	E	I
R	R	L	I	E	I	A	O	S	L	A
D	B	L	T	L	F	L	C	G	I	R
A	L	C	F	N	C	A	D	K	T	T
E	N	I	S	A	C	C	O	M	S	R
S	L	I	P	P	E	R	L	L	U	I

Word Builder

Using the nine letters provided, can you answer these clues? Every answer must include the highlighted letter C. Which farming area uses all nine letters?

R	U	N
S	C	O
L	E	E

5 Letters
Filthy money
Small imperial
  weight
Genetic replica
Near
Hints

Clean vigorously
Damn
Devon cake

6 Letters
Male relatives
Save

Televise
Diplomat
Hags
Origin
Route
Stomach sores

7 Letters
Advise
Reprimand
Repeat
  performances

StepRiddle

To begin with, I am dark as jet.

Change my first and I'm baggy, not tight yet.

When my next is altered I become a high pile.

My third is amended and I glue, adhere to a tile.

My penultimate's changed, revealing a pong, reek or smell.

At the last, change my last, and I defend a bee well.

What was I, what did I become, and what did I turn out to be?

Killer Sudoku

The normal rules of Sudoku apply. Place a digit from 1-9 in each empty square so that each row, column and 3x3 block contains all the digits from 1-9. In addition, the digits in each inner shape (marked by dots) must add up to the number in the top corner of that box. No digit can be repeated within an inner shape.

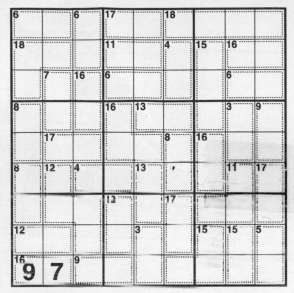

Lettersets

Complete the crossword grid using the letters listed for each row and column. Cracking this one relies on anagram-solving and cross-referencing between Across and Down words.

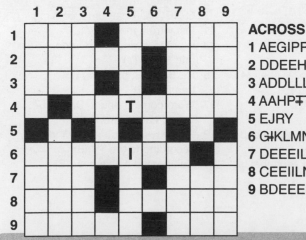

ACROSS
1 AEGIPPST
2 DDEEHLOU
3 ADDLLLO
4 AAHPTTWY
5 EJRY
6 GIKLMNSU
7 DEEEILY
8 CEEIILNR
9 BDEEERWY

DOWN
1 ADEILPST
2 CEIIJLLU
3 EEGLLPRU
4 ABDKR
5 DEILLPTY
6 AEHIN
7 EEGHNOSW
8 ADEOTWYY
9 DDEEEMRY

Mix & Match

You'll have to think just a little bit differently with this mixed-clue crossword. Riddles, anagrams, word association and general knowledge are all included.

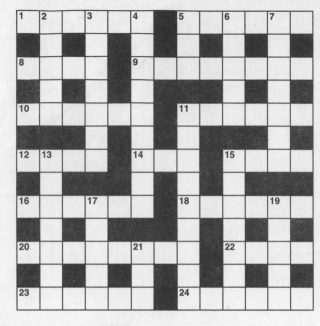

ACROSS

1 Develop from scar, a beetle (6)
5 Peep at part of King Lancelot (6)
8 Word coming before Bean, Milk and Sauce (4)
9 IF CHIMES ring out there'll be trouble! (8)
10 Anagram of PRAISE (6)
11 Vegetable incentive (6)
12 It's marked with an 'x' (4)
14 Take two drops of mocha and end up with tea! (3)
15 Quote sounds like it's to be seen (4)
16 Anagram of WARDER (6)
18 Venues are as NEAR AS destroyed (6)
20 Come to a complete halt at the end of a sentence (4,4)
22 Ninth letter of the Greek alphabet is a tiny thing! (4)
23 And so on he'd scored (6)
24 Anagram of ITCHES (6)

DOWN

2 Brags about birds! (5)
3 Anagram of RETAILS (7)
4 Backside for each vehicle – it's found at the fairground (6,3)
5 Fuel gossip (3)
6 How nature may respond to a vacuum? (5)
7 O HECTOR can produce a cigar (7)
11 Fishy fruit, maybe? (4,5)
13 Word following Hot, Outdoor and Trivial (7)
15 HE'S RICH, breaking up treasure (7)
17 Word coming before Dresser, Guards and Rarebit (5)
19 Room where you might find cash according to the TV (5)
21 Half pasted a little bear (3)

Missing Links

The three words in each of these clues have a fourth word in common, and that's your answer. For instance, the clue to 7 Across, 'Handle • Hole • Post (3)' gives you the answer MAN (Manhandle, Manhole, Postman).

ACROSS

1 Face • Let • Tissue (4)
4 Hook • Nothing • Winger (4)
7 Handle • Hole • Post (3)
8 Band • Bypass • Flu (7)
10 Blades • Coaster • Steam (6)
12 Garden • Grudges • Polar (4)
13 Black • Boot • Wing (4)
15 Box • Distress • Smoke (6)
19 Camel • *Nights* • Saudi (7)
20 Mini • Stop • Trolley (3)
21 Cell • Ginger • Stitch (4)
22 Cotton • Hose • Off (4)

DOWN

2 Boat • Root • Suez (5)
3 Elephant • State • Trader (5)
4 Chance • Post • Week (4)
5 Feed • Labour • Police (5)
6 Pine • Plant • Stand (8)
9 Driving • *Hands* • *Whisper* (8)
11 Detector • In • Low (3)
12 Paper • Pipes • Tea (3)
14 Bar • Flip • Weather (5)
16 Circle • City • Tube (5)
17 Art • Gas • Savage (5)
18 Clip • Feature • Set (4)

Take five

At times, we're unable to concentrate because we have so much on our mind. Perhaps we're so stressed and busy that when we stop and try to concentrate on something, our mind is quite simply unable to slow down. Try to programme brief 'quiet times' into your daily schedule to train the 'puppy'. You'll find that the more often you do this, the easier it will be to bring stillness to your mind in this way.

A final note

If your concentration has suddenly worsened, or if you think you might be depressed, go and see your doctor: sometimes, poor concentration can have other causes that your doctor may be able to help you with.

I hope you've enjoyed the addition of a puppy to your daily life, and that the exercises are helpful.

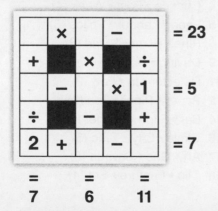

Set Square

Place one each of the digits 1-9 in each grid to make the sums work. We've put in some of the numbers to start you off. Sums should be solved from left to right, or from top to bottom.

Grid 1:

	×		−		= 23
+	■	×	■	÷	
	−		×	1	= 5
÷	■	−	■	+	
2	+		−		= 7

= 7   = 6   = 11

Grid 2:

9	−		+		= 13
×	■	+	■	+	
	×		+		= 9
÷	■	÷	■	÷	
	+		−	3	= 8

= 3   = 1   = 5

Codeword

Can you crack the code and fill in the crossword grid? Each letter of the alphabet makes at least one appearance in the grid, and is represented by the same number wherever it appears. The three letters we've decoded should help you to identify other letters and words in the grid.

9		16		22		8	16	22		24		20		17 P
22	16	8	20	14	23	21		23	6	1	9	26	8	16 R
24		26		8		23		14		16		5		8 O
8	17	9	6	1	23		18	14	9	19	24	4	20	17
16				24		9				23				23
22	9	14	14	8	8	13		24	26	16	20	15	23	16
		20		13		24		5		12		4		14
3	1	10	17		24	7	9	16	10		7	9	25	12
1		22		24		23		20		9		15		
22	14	8	9	26	23	16		17	23	13	24	20	11	23
20				23				26		19				25
14	1	15	23	7	9	16	10		26	1	16	13	20	17
9		20		9		1		9		14		9		23
13	9	26	1	16	9	14		19	14	9	2	20	23	16
26		23		21		23	19	8		16		14		26

A B C D E F G H I J K L M N Ø P Q R S T U V W X Y Z

1	2	3	4	5	6	7	8 O	9	10	11	12	13
14	15	16 R	17 P	18	19	20	21	22	23	24	25	26

Boxwise

Can you place the three-letter groups in the boxes, so that neighbouring boxes always make a six-letter word, like PAR-DON or DON-ATE? We've placed one group to start you off.

ADS		RAF
BAL		SAL
FIA		SAM
FLE		SCO
INE		~~TRI~~
PLE		URS

Number Jig

All of these numbers will fit in the grid. How quickly can you get the numbers placed?

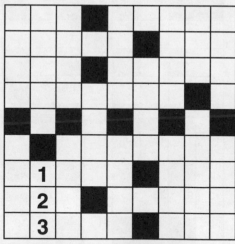

3 Digits	4 Digits		
114	1247	5749	71090
~~123~~	1354	7249	76221
124	1369	7421	76227
213	3000	7514	93089
420	3429		95436
423	4029	5 Digits	
777	5091	25225	7 Digits
813	5629	50181	3249761
		56230	4293167

Who and Where?

Here's a wordsearch, which you solve as normal. First off, though, you have to work out what you're looking for in the grid. There are fourteen celebrity anagrams listed, and you have to work out who each celebrity is. The anagrams are listed in alphabetical order of celebrity, and in some cases the anagrams hint at the celebrity.

N	S	R	O	B	E	R	T	D	E	N	I	R	O	V
R	O	M	P	A	U	L	M	E	R	T	O	N	I	J
O	O	S	A	A	T	U	U	S	X	S	T	C	M	U
N	N	W	R	I	B	I	Z	C	J	Z	T	N	N	L
A	O	D	A	E	L	D	N	H	V	O	X	W	T	I
N	R	E	P	N	D	L	C	A	R	B	O	F	N	E
K	E	S	L	Z	A	N	I	I	T	R	P	V	K	W
E	M	S	B	E	I	T	A	W	B	U	O	G	I	A
A	A	E	I	O	D	B	K	N	E	L	R	H	H	L
T	C	E	R	U	F	M	O	I	A	I	X	N	E	T
I	D	L	F	C	R	D	O	K	N	I	B	R	C	E
N	I	K	K	T	R	C	Q	N	M	S	L	B	W	R
G	V	H	Y	O	Y	D	M	J	D	Q	O	L	O	S
I	A	G	G	N	P	W	A	O	W	S	J	N	I	R
M	D	O	O	W	T	S	A	E	T	N	I	L	C	G

Actor: OLD WEST ACTION

Singer: LO, IMBIBER WAILS

Politician: MAN, I RAVED DOC

Actor: ERRON ON BIDET

Actress: NO ALIENS, DARLING

Singer: NOT ARENA KING

Politician: OR WRONG BOND

Comedian: ANORAK'S IN TOWN

Actress: RITUAL JEWELS

Singer: A TRITER NUN

TV presenter: MENDS NOODLE

Actor: COSTUMIER

Comedian: MANURE PLOT

Singer: A VOICE MIRTH BACK

Fitword

When all of the listed words have been placed correctly in the grid, which one is left over?

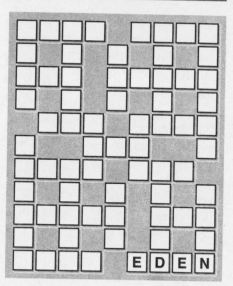

3 letters	4 letters	5 letters
Ado	Acts	Curio
Bet	Both	Hurry
Hue	Earl	Older
Ohm	~~Eden~~	Raved
Pry	Harm	Tudor
Tax	Hate	Waxed
Try	Hewn	
Vet	Stun	**6 letters**
Why	Whom	Scythe
		Swathe

The mental blackboard in daily life

It will be easy to see how the mental blackboard works by providing a few examples. Have you ever started reading something – an instruction booklet for a new mp3 player, say – and felt your brain going to mush after a few lines? Did you take in any information at all? How about dealing with a bank manager concerning a loan or mortgage or something similar – have you felt as if the person's words were bouncing off your ears and were coming too quickly for you to take things in? Have you ever wondered if you've been given the right change in a shop or restaurant but gave up doing the calculation in your head because you couldn't keep track of the sums? What about planning a holiday – do you feel mentally overwhelmed juggling the times you can be away, flights, accommodation and more?

As you can see, we use the mental blackboard every day, so making improvements can have a big impact in our lives. We'll start exploring the changes you can make on page 142.

Sudoku

Place a number in each empty square so that each row, each column and each 2x2 block contains all the numbers from 1-4.

1	4		2
	2		
	3		4
4	1		3

4	2	1	3
2	1	3	4

	3	2	4
2			3
3			2
	2	3	

Logical

Try solving this little logical problem in your head before putting pen to paper.

Three children had finished primary school, and were enjoying the summer break before moving on to secondary school, with varying degrees of trepidation. Ashley wasn't going to the mixed school, while Tommy would be moving to the School of Hard Knocks. The School of Rock wasn't the boys' school, and the School for Scoundrels would not be welcoming Georgia in September. If the School of Hard Knocks wasn't the boys' school, which child went to which school, and was it a boys', girls' or mixed establishment?

Jigsaw

Use the jigsaw pieces to recreate this completed crossword. We've only listed clues for the rows of Across words, but the pattern of the grid should help you, being symmetrical from top left to bottom right.

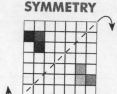

SYMMETRY

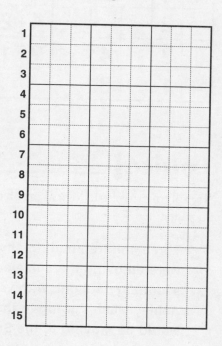

ACROSS

1 Animal foot
2 Roman house • Paddle
3 Sibling's daughter
4 Bird's perch
5 Fitted (in)
6 Ballet skirt
7 Advantage
8 Small bottle
9 Serving platter
10 Old Russian ruler
11 Showing enmity
12 Competing
13 Wireless
14 Old name for beer • ___ Butler, hero of *Gone with the Wind*
15 Ironic (as of a smile)

Mix & Match

This mixed-clue crossword will get you thinking in lots of different ways. Riddles, anagrams, word association and general knowledge are all included.

ACROSS

1 Don't be so worried about being unaware (8)
5 Headless, Lance finds fruit (4)
9 Mild Indian creamy coconut curry sauce (5)
10 It may be a sign of swimming or mourning (7)
11 Word linking Garden, Rack and Sun (4)
12 Text or book of words of an opera (8)
14 Anagram of STEALS (6)
15 LETS US struggle and fight (6)
18 Dressing sounds like Popeye's girl (5,3)
20 Help with a punt (4)
23 Care in advance and play the part (7)
24 Word following Red, Spanish and Spring (5)
25 Anagram of TIER (4)
26 Percussion instrument associated with Bermuda? (8)

DOWN

1 Inventor can create, right? (5)
2 Word coming before Energy, System and Wreck (7)
3 Begin with lots of aerated mud for fertile soil (4)
4 Electricity's still! (6)
6 Only some MULTIPLEX ACTING is spot on! (5)
7 A symptom of a cold's revealed when Lancashire's flower centre changes to North (3,4)
8 Find US A ROOM, uncontrolled and passionate! (7)
13 Somehow TREE VALE loses a hare (7)
14 Proverbially swearing cavalryman (7)
16 Is this your brother or your sister? It doesn't matter – it's either! (7)
17 Anagram of INBRED (6)
19 Nobel laureate PINTER has no right to be confused and clumsy (5)
21 Hint of colour seen in PAINTING EASEL (5)
22 Work schedule rises with the second-half NARRATOR (4)

Practise using your mental blackboard

This exercise is a good way of showing you what I mean by the mental blackboard.

Below, you'll find a list of numbers ranging from 1 to 5. Your exercise is to add each pair of numbers together, but there's a twist. First you add 1 to 5, giving 6. Now for the twist: next you add not the 2 and the 4, but the 5 and the 2, giving 7. The answers are in highlighted below the list of numbers, to make things clearer.

1	5	2	4	3	2	1	2	5	4	3	4
	6	7									

Now, fill in the rest of the numbers, and turn to page 147.

Now, fill in the rest of the numbers, and turn to page 147.

Hide and Seek

How quickly can you identify the squares in which each of the numbered shapes appears?

Dateline

Work out the answers to the clues to discover the date in the shaded space – a significant date in sport. Calculators strictly forbidden!

ACROSS

1 Anagram of 13 Down
4 24 x 17 + 273
6 6006 x 6 + 13,790
8 1482 ÷ 6
9 33 x 33
11 25% of 3 Down
12 Cube root of 1000
13 Mystery date
16 2008 – 1964 + 48
17 Three score and ten
19 1091 + 3223 + 4122
21 1 Across – 11 Down
22 (123,907 – 16,789) ÷ 3
24 12.5% of 2608
25 7 x 20 x 7

DOWN

1 40,707 ÷ 9
2 A fifth of 123,505
3 952 ÷ 14
4 13 Down + 20 Down
5 11 Down + 25 Across
7 5 Down + 9 Across
10 Pounds in 58 stone
11 5p pieces in £5.50
13 18 squared
14 3313 + 2925 + 2527
15 A third of 226,107
16 50,050 – 27,772 – 12,465
18 39,168 ÷ 12 + 16
20 Hours in two weeks
23 72 x 6 ÷ 8 + 23

Sweet Success

Which of the ten pieces has been cut from the cake?

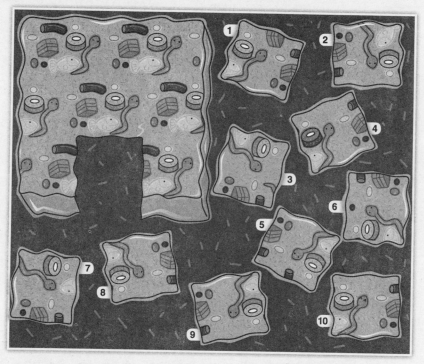

Futoshiki

Fill the blank squares so that each row and column contains all the numbers 1, 2 and 3 in the smaller grids, and 1, 2, 3 and 4 in the larger grid. Use the given numbers and the symbols that tell you if the number in the square is larger (>) or smaller (<) than the number next to it.

Number Jig

All but one of these numbers will fit in the grid. How quickly can you get the numbers placed, and which is left over?

3 Digits	2478	5 Digits
238	2879	40044
240	2946	46102
432	3984	50620
462	4215	54602
~~538~~	4318	72108
563	5832	72842
	6830	
4 Digits	6932	7 Digits
1384	7172	3825671
1385	7610	9461283
1480	8200	
1913	9124	

Arroword

Just follow the arrows to write your answers in the grid. A handful of anagram clues will get you thinking differently.

LEMONS (anagram)	Pig's home		Hate, loathe		__ carte, from the menu (1,2)		Cutting (bread)	Edible portion of a nut
Porridge ingredient							NEEDS (anagram)	
Gusto		Golf stroke on the green	SIDLE (anagram)					
			On behalf of	CAPER (anagram)				
Soldier's civilian dress					Small hotel or pub			
			Impression					
Really keen on	Real				Hair-style fixer			

Codeword

Can you crack the code and fill in the crossword grid? Each letter of the alphabet makes at least one appearance in the grid, and is represented by the same number wherever it appears. The five letters we've decoded should help you to identify other letters and words in the grid.

5		18		25		5	11	25		16		6		25
8	5	10	8	12	25	21		19	5	2	14	2	25	21
21		2		5		7		20		24		25		24
22	14	26	5	1	25		13	23	21	1	25	14	2	5
14				2		22				2				6
8	25	24	7	22	26	21		1	2	9	6	5	26	2
		5		26		6		23		21		12		26
12	5	9	8		20	14	5	6	13		4	2	26	20
25		25		10		25		2		24		8		
15	12	22	10	26	24	23		15	12	22	4	2	26	20
											O	W	I	N	G
1				24			23		24					5
22	26	12	22	22	7	25	14		21	7	2	16	25	14
16		2		10		19		5		6		5		5
25	3	25	24	1	25	19		21	25	2	17	2	26	20
14		19		13		23	5	6		1		26		25

A B C D E F Ø H ✗ J K L M ✗ Ø P Q R S T U V ✗ X Y Z

1	2	3	4	5	6	7	8	9	10	11	12	13
	I		W									
14	15	16	17	18	19	20	21	22	23	24	25	26
						G		O				N

Practise using your mental blackboard

How did you do with the exercise on page 142? Here's the completed list:

1	5	2	4	3	2	1	2	5	4	3	4
	6	7	6	7	5	3	3	7	9	7	7

You have to do quite a bit of writing, and rubbing out, on your mental blackboard to execute this task. That's especially the case if you're hearing the numbers rather than seeing them. In detail, the four elements that make up this task are:

1 Add the pair of numbers and remember the answer (the first '6' in our example).

2 Mentally 'rub out' the 6 because you won't need it again, and you don't want to get it mixed up
with the next numbers you need.

3 Remember what the last number is (5 in our example).

4 Listen to the next number (2) and add it to the remembered 5.

Try this again with the list below, and write the answers underneath.

5	2	3	2	1	4	3	5	4	4	2

Now try it again, this time with someone reading the numbers out loud at a slowish pace (one number every three seconds). Get your friend to write out the numbers and the answers, and to read them out so you can check your answers. If you get them all right, increase the speed at which the numbers are read out (every two seconds).

This is excellent training for your working memory. It's exactly the sort of task you do in your head when you work out whether you are being short-changed, or what the 20% off sign in the sale means you will actually have to pay.

Turn to page 149 to discover how you can exercise your mental blackboard when you're out and about.

Staircase

When these types of fabric are correctly fitted in the rows of the grid, another will appear down the diagonal staircase.

ALPACA
CANVAS
FUSTIAN
GAUZE
MERINO
NANKEEN
TWILL

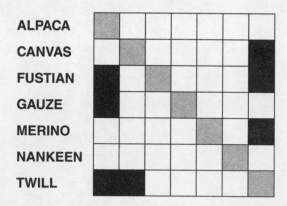

Mind the Gap

Can you place a well-known three-letter word in the spaces of each row to complete the seven-letter word? Do it correctly, and the shaded letters should spell out something associated with galleries.

E	X			G	E
C	A			S	E
T			H	E	S
A	G	I			E
F	I	S			Y
S	C			A	L
E			O	M	E
S			E	N	D

Exercise your mental blackboard in shops and restaurants

Exercising your mental blackboard isn't limited to theoretical situations – you can do mental arithmetic calculations throughout the day. Once you're comfortable working with numbers, follow these tips about how to use your mental blackboard in your daily life:

- *When you're in a supermarket, keep a running total of your spend as you put the items in your trolley (this can be approximate rather than exact – see below for details).*

- *Make a habit of estimating what your change should be in a shop. Try to do this in your head, so that you can predict what the assistant will give you back.*

Clearly, adding up the exact price of every single item you put in your trolley would slow you down too much. However, it is simple to calculate a rough running total on your mental blackboard by rounding up or down to the nearest pound. For example, if something costs £1.26, just call it £1, and if something costs £3.63, round it up to £4. In other words, where the pence on a price is fifty or below, round it down, and if it's 51 or over, round the price up.

By doing this, the roundings up and roundings down should roughly cancel each other out, so you will have a good approximate total of what your total spend will be before you get to the till. This can provide a pleasant diversion while trudging around the supermarket.

Turn to page 160 to begin learning about another means of improving your mental blackboard.

Pathfinder

Beginning with LOAFING, and moving up, down, left or right, one letter at a time, trace a path – if you can be bothered – through sixteen words meaning 'lazy'.

G	D	D	P	K	L	S	L	C	R	A
N	I	O	L	C	A	X	A	I	G	H
O	R	K	S	H	O	R	O	U	S	T
W	A	C	I	Y	U	G	I	P	T	E
E	L	I	S	L	A	N	D	R	O	L
V	I	A	K	C	H	S	R	I	S	S
I	D	D	A	A	L	I	E	M	S	G
S	L	E	I	U	G	G	L	T	H	N
S	A	P	N	L	S	S	E	F	I	I
T	I	M	D	E	D	S	E	N	A	F
N	E	L	O	T	A	V	R	E	O	L

Sudoku

Use your powers of reasoning to place numbers in the grid, so that each row, each column and each 3x3 block contains the numbers 1-9.

1		4				2		9
				5				
9			1	8	2			4
		2				3		
	3		2		8		4	
		8	7		5	1		
		7	6		3	5		
2	1						3	8
3			8	1	9			2

Lose a Letter

Cross out one letter in each square to leave a completed crossword. You may have to think ahead to rule out some red herrings along the way.

Word Builder

Using the nine letters provided, can you answer these clues? Every answer must include the highlighted letter N. Which template uses all nine letters?

R	I	L
E	**N**	T
P	U	B

5 Letters
Poker-like flower
Ocean-going vessel
To the time that
Charred
Dried plum
Salt water

6 Letters
Root vegetable
Wolf-like
More weedy
Immature
Gambler
Identity parade (4-2)

7 Letters
Roman magistrate
Rotary engine
Less sharp

Missing Links

The three words in each of these clues have a fourth word in common, and that's your answer. For instance, the clue to 4 Across, 'Cuts • Horse • Point (5)' gives you the answer POWER (Power cuts, Horsepower, Power point).

ACROSS

1 Body • Land • Up (5)
4 Cuts • Horse • Point (5)
7 Flag • General • Group (7)
8 Bred • Equipped • Suited (3)
9 Fire • Heat • Water (9)
13 Book • Cross • Grid (9)
17 Do • Opener • Tin (3)
18 Hall • Pianist • Pop (7)
20 Fancy • Head • Rehearsal (5)
21 Clerical • Human • Typing (5)

DOWN

1 Arms • House • Parking (6)
2 Cord • Let • Tide (3)
3 Rubbing • Tacks • Top (5)
4 Car • Giant • Red (5)
5 Instructions • Permission • Warning (7)
6 Leading • Model • Title (4)
10 Days • Steve • Ways (7)
11 Bow • Pin • Rack (3)
12 Get • Half • Nature (6)
14 Auto • Group • Soft (5)
15 Cooker • Mountain • Rifle (5)
16 Drop • Rain • Test (4)
19 Drum • Thick • Wheat (3)

Backwords

The answers to this crossword are all here, along with extra letters where the black squares should be. Can you black out any unwanted letters to leave a grid that matches the clues (which are out of order)? The finished grid will have full symmetry.

J	O	B	S	L	I	P	S	P	A	N
U	N	I	A	F	A	D	A	A	R	E
S	A	N	T	A	L	E	V	I	C	T
T	E	G	E	S	D	P	E	N	D	T
W	H	O	S	T	I	L	I	T	Y	M
M	A	N	Y	E	V	O	C	H	A	A
I	M	A	N	N	E	R	I	S	M	Y
A	P	V	E	I	R	I	M	A	R	C
B	L	O	W	N	O	N	A	C	H	O
U	O	I	L	G	A	G	S	K	I	L
T	I	D	E	A	R	N	U	S	E	D

ACROSS

- Aggression
- Water current
- Second-hand
- Breadth
- Triangular Mexican chip
- Work tasks
- Wisecrack
- ___ Claus, Father Christmas
- Transient craze
- Behavioural trait
- Remove (from the premises)
- Carried by the wind

DOWN

- Lean against
- Cured pork
- Bemoaning
- Unfeeling
- Fair
- After tax
- Potato-like tuber
- Numbers game
- Hessian bags
- Daub with colour
- Keep away from
- Making secure

Picture Pair

How quickly can you spot the two identical pictures?

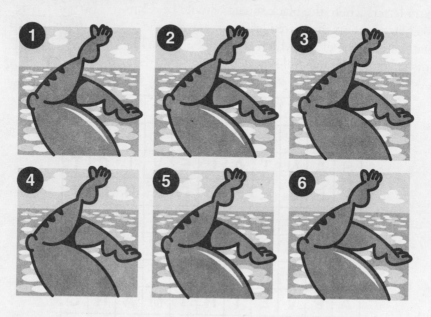

Stage Directions

Don't worry about pens now – just concentrate on your jazz hands. There are fifteen one-word musicals to find in the grid.

H	A	I	R	S	P	R	A	Y
L	L	S	E	T	O	T	A	N
C	O	L	I	V	E	R	O	C
H	A	Q	E	R	I	O	A	C
E	E	R	A	P	D	T	A	H
S	S	B	O	A	S	M	A	I
S	A	H	G	U	E	D	G	C
C	E	I	D	L	S	I	O	A
U	R	I	O	B	G	E	Y	G
B	G	T	O	M	M	Y	L	O
A	M	O	H	A	L	K	O	F

Six Pack

Can you place digits in the empty triangles, so that the numbers in each hexagon add up to 25? Only single digits between 1 and 9 can be used, and no two numbers in any hexagon may be the same.

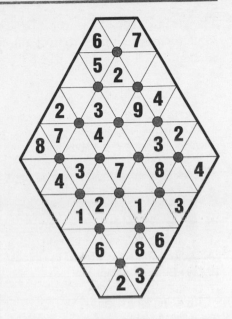

Drop Quote

Here's a quotation from Bertrand Russell on wisdom. The words have dropped out of position into the columns below. Can you restore the quote?

	WHOLE				
ALWAYS				THEMSELVES,	
			FULL		DOUBTS.

THE	~~WHOLE~~	CERTAIN	~~FULL~~	OF	BUT
WISER	PEOPLE	PROBLEM	OF	THE	~~DOUBTS~~
~~ALWAYS~~	SO	SO	WITH	FANATICS	ARE
IS	THAT	FOOLS	AND	~~THEMSELVES~~	WORLD

Dilemma Crossword

The clues for these crosswords have been mixed up. As you solve them, you'll need to work out which answer goes in each grid.

ACROSS

1 Wrist shackles • Religious quiz instruction

7 Book of maps • Having cargo aboard

8 Supply with weapons again • Powdered tobacco for inhaling

10 Per person • Rain heavily, pour

11 Small hawk • Straw for baskets

14 Choice • Infuse slowly into the mind

15 Lip • Body of a ship

17 Costume, outfit (3-2) • Travelling tribesman

19 Of little weight • Airman

20 Demote, place in a lower class • People who take out loans

DOWN

2 Junkies • Physical disorder

3 Simple • Unpleasantly wet

4 Dislodge from a saddle • Plant-based (medicine)

5 Winter illness • Expanse of water

6 Thorny shrub with red berries • ___ *Love*, Leona Lewis hit

9 Person who shares your apartment • Column made from a single stone

12 Paired • Person rummaging for food

13 Stiff and awkward in movement and manner • Breakfast fish

16 Shine in the dark • Practise boxing

18 Pair • Cow's low

Mobile Quotes

We've put four quotations in code, using the numbers on a mobile keypad. So, for instance, the first letter of the first quote could be G, H or I. Can you work out what Lord Byron said?

'4 84465 843 96778 96626 8428 3837 3947833 96853 4283 6233 2 626 63 8379 72772253 7378828466 – 8439 273 255 238837 8426 87 263 84347 328587 7824 27 8439 273 6878 674446283 9484 687735837.'

'4 4283 47328 46737 8428 93 74255 5683 3224 68437 255 687 54837 27 6824 27 43 93 423 63837 6277433 28 255.'

'2637422 47 2 66335 63 36723 263 3733366 263 6633728466 – 9484 255 843 2627736377 263 78336377 63 487 736753.'

'259297 52844 9436 968 226. 48 47 24327 63342463.'

Sudoku

Use your powers of reasoning to place numbers in the grid, so that each row, each column and each 3x3 block contains the numbers 1-9.

	1							
						4	7	
4		9		5			2	
					7		1	
8	3					9		
5	9	1						
		2	5			4		
9	5		8	4				1
	6		3	9		5		

Alpha-Beater

Every letter of the alphabet has been removed from this crossword once. How quickly can you put all 26 back? Use the A-Z list to cross off letters as you use them.

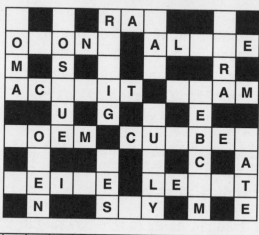

| A | B | C | D | E | F | G | H | I | J | K | L | M |
| N | O | P | Q | R | S | T | U | V | W | X | Y | Z |

Set Square

Place one each of the digits 1-9 in each grid to make the sums work. We've put in some of the numbers to start you off. Sums should be solved from left to right, or from top to bottom.

Elimination

All but two of the listed words fall into one of the four categories. Put these leftover words together, and what word or phrase do they make?

CATEGORIES

Toys • Reptiles • Music genres • Words coming before 'FLY'

Rattle	Doll	Hop
Hover	Turtle	Fire
House	Butter	Dragon
Scotch	Kite	Lizard
Teddy	Snake	Jazz
Crocodile	Green	Iguana
Rock	Skates	
Blues	Reggae	

Reading Matter

Here's a top ten list of the nation's most borrowed authors from libraries. Spend two minutes fixing as much information as you can in your mind, then turn to page 160.

1	James Patterson	Thriller
2	Jacqueline Wilson	Children's
3	Daisy Meadows	Children's
4	Josephine Cox	Romance
5	Nora Roberts	Romance
6	Danielle Steele	Romance
7	Ian Rankin	Crime
8	Mick Inkpen	Children's
9	Janet & Allen Ahlberg	Children's
10	Francesca Simon	Children's

Learn to GASP

GASP is a means of giving your mental blackboard a chance to work so that you can think on your feet more easily.

GASP is what you should do if you feel: flummoxed by the insurance saleman's pitch; confused by the instructions for your new mobile phone; overwhelmed by the complicated language of the small print on the contract in front of you.

GASP means:

Get control over the information flow
Anxiety is distracting – don't think about how you're doing
Split the information up into smaller chunks
Practise using your mental blackboard

I explore these in greater depth, starting on page 162.

Reading Matter _____

See if you can fill in the blanks in this list from page 159.

1 James _____
2 _____ Wilson   Thriller
3 Daisy Meadows   Children's
4 Josephine _____
5 _____ Roberts   _____
6 _____ _____   Romance
7 _____ Rankin   Romance
8 Mick Inkpen   Crime
9 ___ and ___ Ahlberg   _____
10 _____ Simon   Children's
                         Children's

Three to One

You'll have to think ahead to complete this crossword. You have a choice of three words to put in each space, but which will fit with its neighbours?

ACROSS

1 Scan • Span • Swan
4 Life • Musk • Ruse
7 Ace • Egg • Out
8 Succumb • Tactile • Through
10 Melody • Murder • Purple
12 Chad • Sled • Tear
13 Ruse • Tape • Tone
15 Séance • Slight • Twilit
19 Claimed • Cloches • Clothed
20 Van • Vet • Via
21 Skid • Skim • Skin
22 Earn • Eels • Ewer

DOWN

2 Cigar • Petal • Water
3 Naïve • Nasal • Nutty
4 Deck • Lock • Mock
5 Frill • Flute • Slush
6 Despotic • Dogmatic • Vampiric
9 Bedstead • Evidence • Hermetic
11 Die • One • Pie
12 Chi • Ski • Tea
14 Prank • Prose • Sidle
16 Badge • Ladle • Waste
17 Giver • Levee • Novel
18 Amid • Avid • Aver

First GASP
Get control over the information flow

Everyone *gets flummoxed if information comes too quickly. Salespeople often use this fact to browbeat people into buying – they present information so fast that they try to make their victim (you!) feel stupid because you can't take all the information in. If you feel stupid, you feel embarrassed, and if you feel embarrassed, you may just say, 'Oh I'll buy it,' simply to get out of the embarrassing situation.*

The same thing can happen if you're asking a waiter for information about the menu. The waiter may speak faster than you can take in their words. Often this is unintentional – a good waiter knows the menu inside out, but doesn't realise that it's impossible for you to take in the information at the speed he's saying it.

So, for the above situations (and many more!), the first rule of GASP is that YOU take control over how fast the information is coming at you. There are many ways of doing this, but the easiest and most effective are:

1. *As soon as you sense you're not taking in any information, say, 'Hold on a minute, can you say that again?' Do not, on any account, feel embarrassed to say this. Remember, it's impossible to take in all the information coming at you for the first time.*

2. *Repeat what you think you've just been told, and ask if that's right. YOU are in control now, because you are asking them to check what you are saying and decide whether it's right or not.*

3. *If you are reading, don't try to take in everything at once. Say to yourself, 'I think this is what I've just read,' then go back and check against your summary.*

You'll find our second GASP on page 169.

Kakuro

Simple addition and a bit of logical thinking will solve this one. You must write a digit in each white square so that the digits in each block add up to the total in the box above or to the left. 1-9 are the only digits to use and, although you may find a digit repeated in a row, it must not be repeated in the same block. We've solved one block for you.

Mini Jigsaw

Fit the pieces in the grid to spell out a film term in each row.

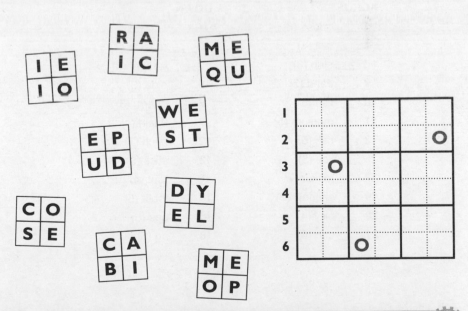

First Thoughts

Fill in the blank in each clue to make a well-known word or phrase, then write your answers in the grid. We've solved one clue to start you off.

ACROSS

1 ___ goose (6)
4 ___ call (4)
8 ___ strip (3)
9 ___ band (7)
10 ___ fish (5)
11 ___ medium (5)
13 ___ hall (5)
15 ___ line (5)
17 ___ maker (7)
19 ___ shadow (3)
20 ___ billy (4)
21 ___ quo (6)

DOWN

1 ___ war (5)
2 ___ tension (7)
3 ___ nought (5)
5 ___ side (3)
6 ___ charm (5)
7 ___ basin (4)
12 ___ pitch (7)
13 ___ stick (5)
14 ___ root (4)
15 ___ tooth (5)
16 ___ ups (5)
18 ___ rig (3)

Verse Strings

Who knew there were so many types of verse made up by bards? There are fifteen listed here. Filling the grid is on the cards.

3 letters
LAY
ODE

4 letters
SAGA

5 letters
DIRGE
ELEGY
HAIKU
IDYLL
LYRIC

6 letters
BALLAD

7 letters
BALLADE

RONDEAU

8 letters
PALINODE

9 letters
DITHYRAMB
ROUNDELAY

10 letters
QUATORZAIN
VILLANELLE

Futoshiki

Fill the blank squares so that each row and column contains all the numbers 1, 2 and 3 in the smaller grids, and 1, 2, 3 and 4 in the larger grid. Use the given numbers and the symbols that tell you if the number in the square is larger (>) or smaller (<) than the number next to it.

Sudoku

Use your powers of reasoning to place numbers in the grid, so that each row, each column and each 3x3 block contains the numbers 1-9.

2						8	9	6
	3	7					2	4
6	4	1		7				
				5	4		7	
9	8		3		2			
	9		5				4	7
5					3	8		9

Arroword

Just follow the arrows to write your answers in the grid. Are the anagram clues a help or hindrance?

Judo or karate, eg (7,3)	Conscious	Shake-speare's jealous Moor ▼	▼	Candle material	▼	Bullfighter	▼	And so on (abbr)	▼
►	▼								
Ship of the desert		ATOM (anagram)		In case		OVER (anagram)		__ Sampras, tennis great	
►				▼	Sharp knock	▼		▼	Was in front
Person to admire and imitate (4,5) ►									▼
►					VETO (anagram) ►				
SHALE (anagram)	Walked unsteadily ►								

Vowel Play

Do you recognise all these words without their vowels? Just put the vowels back correctly to complete the crossword.

F		R		Y			Z		R	
						R		S		N
F		W				M			L	M
F		N		S					N	T
	Z		S	T		D			N	T
B		S						N		Y
R		S	T	Y		P		T	Y	
						L		R		
K		Y		M				N	N	
			L		M					L
N		T		D		B		D	L	Y

Logical

Try solving this logical problem in your head before putting pen to paper.

Three consecutive visitors to the local dogs' home each adopted a dog. From the information given below, work out who adopted which dog, what type of dog it was and its favourite treat. The favourite treat of the dog adopted by Ed, which wasn't the Labrador, was chicken. Ted adopted Ben, while Ged only had eyes for the mongrel. Sam's favourite treat wasn't steak, while the pug was named Rex. Tuna was the favourite treat of one of the dogs.

Pattern Maker

If a dotted line indicates a cut, and an uninterrupted line indicates a fold, which of the five patterns is produced when you fold and cut the square of paper as indicated?

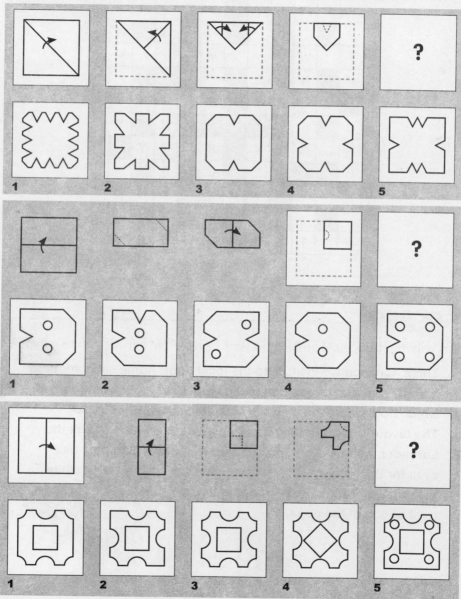

Second GASP

Anxiety is distracting – don't think about how you're doing.

Have you ever started thinking about what your feet are doing as you walked down stairs, and felt how it made you unsteady and more likely to fall?

The same can happen if you fill up your mental blackboard with worrying thoughts like, 'I can't take this in – oh this is terrible... they'll think I'm stupid... I'm in such a muddle...' and so on.

So instead of worrying about how well you are thinking on your feet, just focus on the G of GASP – get control over the information flow.

Now, it's time for the third GASP.

Third GASP

Split the information up into smaller chunks

*When you read the instructions for a new device, your first response is often, 'Oh this is too complicated' or 'I'll have to ask Alan next door to read this for me...'. You **don't** have to do this.*
Here is what to do:

- *Just break the instructions up into as many small chunks as you like.*
- *Focus your attention just on the first small part. Got it in your mind by repeating what it says in your own words. If you like, write this down, but as you notice an improvement, you can just remember it.*
- *Then do the same for the second part.*
- *Repeat the first and second parts of the instructions to yourself.*

You can do this when people are speaking to you, using some of the methods of the first GASP I gave you on page 162.

You'll find a Last GASP on page 175.

Dilemma Fitword

Can you fit all the listed words into the two grids? You'll need to do some thinking ahead, and jumping between grids to crack this one.

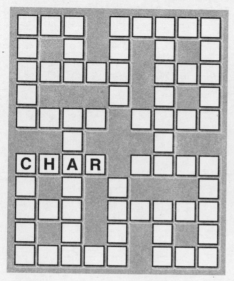

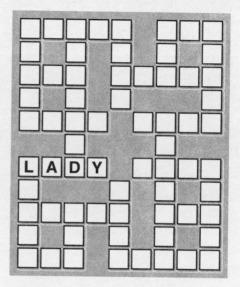

3 Letters	4 Letters	5 Letters	7 Letters
BAG	~~CHAR~~	CABLE	STATURE
BOW	EACH	CACAO	SUBDUED
COG	~~LADY~~	COPED	SUBLIME
GAB	MEAL	CRYPT	SUBSUME
IBO	MESS	EMOTE	
OAK	OAST	LASSO	
SIP	OBOE	LIEGE	
SOU	PURR	OMBRE	
SUB	SOAR	STEAK	
WOK	SOUR	STYLE	
YAK	USED	TASKS	
YOU	USER	TASTE	
		THEIR	
		TIGER	
		UNDER	
		UPSET	

Word Builder

Using the nine letters provided, can you answer these clues?
Every answer must include the highlighted letter C. Which
admirable quality all nine letters?

L	E	T
A	C	E
R	O	N

5 Letters
Jousting spear
Respond
Fishing basket
Genetic replica
Long-legged bird
Verve

6 Letters
Prophet, seer
Wine variety
Brass instrument
Hypnotic state
Juice container
Drink of the gods

7 Letters
Detergent
Vital
Voter
Book-stand
Dark syrup

8 Letters
Charged particle
Orange pigment
  in plants
Move

StepRiddle

To begin with I'm, confusingly, both very and a bit.

Change my first and you'll discover something on which you may sit.

When my next is amended, I'm malice from the spleen.

My third letter is changed to show an outbreak unforeseen.

Next, change my next and you'll find something surplus, what may
remain.

At the last, change my last, and I'm what a boxer does to train.

What was I, what did I become, and what did I turn out to be?

Missing Links

The three words in each of these clues have a fourth word in common, and that's your answer. For instance, 3 Down, 'Doing • Footing • Number (4)' gives you the answer WRONG (Wrongdoing, Wrong footing, Wrong number).

1	**2**		**3** W		**4**		**5**		
6			R						
7			**8** O						**9**
			N						
10		**11**	G			**12**			
13		**14**		**15**	**16**		**17**		
			18						
19							**20**		
	21				**22**				

ACROSS

1 Dance • Motion • Worm (4)
4 Cause • Control • Get (4)
7 Bus • Freshener • Port (3)
8 Egg • Farm • Feather (7)
10 Atomic • Kinetic • Solar (6)
12 Hole • Rawl • Spark (4)
13 Listening • Money • Over (4)
15 Agent • Foreign • Sickness (6)
19 Drinks • Shopping • Tea (7)
20 Fold • Pin • Top (3)
21 Bus • Cock • Full (4)
22 Arum • Tiger • Water (4)

DOWN

2 Extra • Print • Scale (5)
3 Doing • Footing • Number (5)
4 Comer • Developer • Lunch (4)
5 Life • Sit • Water (5)
6 *Angel* • Artist • Moving (8)
9 Cattle • Dress • Fling (8)
11 Charles • Gun • Sting (3)
12 Chick • Cock • Shooter (3)
14 Blood • Good • Indoor (5)
16 Blue • Flush • Jelly (5)
17 Contribution • Organ • Spark (5)
18 Cow • Gym • Way (4)

Codeword

Can you crack the code and fill in the crossword grid? Each letter of the alphabet makes at least one appearance in the grid, and is represented by the same number wherever it appears. The three letters we've decoded should help you to identify other letters and words in the grid.

24		9		4		25	20	8		11		6		25
4	15	24	12	2	8	3		9	24	12	6	15	8	3
25		26		5		3		11		25		25		1
19	25	26	8	14	5		4	6	8	12	25	26	11	10
14				11		4				8				11
8	22	2	11	12	6	2		9	8	14	11	6(C)	25(A)	12(N)
		24		18		10		14		5		10		8
14	5	12	22		20	26	8	25	23		19	26	8	3
11		11		4		13		17		9		18		
21	25	8	2	10	26	5		24	9	4	20	11	12	18
8				13				8		5				26
14	10	10	4	8	12	8	3		4	6	25	26	6	8
11		12		15		16		10		15		25		8
23	8	5	12	10	2	8		20	15	11	7	7	8	3
8		22		20		12	11	14		6		8		5

A B C D E F G H I J K L M N O P Q R S T U V W X Y Z

1	2	3	4	5	6 C	7	8	9	10	11	12 N	13
14	15	16	17	18	19	20	21	22	23	24	25 A	26

One on One

Our final puzzle this time is a straightforward crossword. Don't let that trick you though – while the answers are all quite straightforward, so too are the clues. In fact, the clues are all of just one word, so don't be surprised if you need to think a bit laterally to get the answers. Have fun.

ACROSS

1 Obligation (4)
5 Within (4)
8 Transmitter (5)
10 Unspeaking (4)
12 Peg (3)
13 Ambition (4)
14 Whole (9)
16 Granny (3)
18 Meditates (5)
21 Iron (5)
23 Offender (11)
24 Funny (5)
25 Trees (5)
26 Pigpen (3)
29 Unreal (9)
32 Granary (4)
33 Pole (3)
34 Swag (4)
35 Byroads (5)
36 Exercise (4)
37 Jump (4)

DOWN

1 Jettison (4)
2 Skirt (4)
3 Language (5)
4 Oversleep (3,2)
6 Humour (4)
7 Regime (4)
9 Ruin (11)
11 Amuse (9)
13 Dissenting (9)
15 Student (5)
17 Minds (5)
19 Collection (3)
20 Mole (3)
21 Chart (3)
22 Weight (3)
26 Wander (5)
27 Trill (5)
28 Deftly (4)
29 Amphibian (4)
30 Ringlet (4)
31 End (4)

Last GASP

Practise using your mental blackboard

We can all be lazy, and decide we can't be bothered to do something. That applies to the mental blackboard too – it can be easy to get out of the habit of using it, so it is important to use it whenever you can in everyday life, whether you are shopping, eating out, reading or taking financial advice. **The more you use it, the better you will become at it, and you might also save yourself some money.** *You can also, perhaps, have some fun testing yourself against the cashier or salesman.*

Many of the puzzles in Puzzler Brain Trainer *are great for exercising your mental blackboard – sudoku, for instance, is a great example. So remember to practise using your mental blackboard in as many situations as possible, including doing* Puzzler Brain Trainer. *This way, you have a good chance of improving your ability to think on your feet. Good luck with your brain training.*

Set Square

Place one each of the digits 1-9 in each grid to make the sums work. We've put in some of the numbers to start you off. Sums should be solved from left to right, or from top to bottom.

Grid 1:

	×		−		= 7
+		×		×	
	−		+	1	= 6
−		÷		+	
	+	3	−		= 2

= 4   = 8   = 13

Grid 2:

	+		−	4	= 10
−		÷		×	
1	+		+		= 11
+		+		÷	
	−		×		= 4

= 12   = 9   = 14

Answers

PAGE 2
Fitword

Leftover word: **RIOT**

PAGE 3
Codeword

PAGE 4
Logical

Cara, Questor, 3rd
Sara, Trixie, 1st
Tara, Hathor, 2nd

Moon Dog

Shadow **8**

PAGE 5
Mix & Match

PAGE 6
Staircase

Stock, Buying, Service,
Company, Devalue, Output,
Goods

The business term is: **SURPLUS**

Hide and Seek

1 a6 **2** a3 **3** f6 **4** e3 **5** e2 **6** c4

PAGE 7
Dateline

Date: **29.4.1884** (Oxford
University agreed to
admit female students to
examinations)

PAGE 8
Spaghetti Loopy

Picture **9**

Futoshiki

1	2	3
2	3	1
3	1	2

1	3	2
2	1	3
3	2	1

4	3	1	2
1	2	4	3
2	4	3	1
3	1	2	4

PAGE 9
Number Jig

Leftover number: **5172**

Arroword

The word is: **RATE**

PAGE 10
Codeword

PAGE 11
Staircase

Salve, Styptic, Emetic, Serum,
Potion, Insulin, Antacid.

The medicine is: **STEROID**

Answers

PAGE 12
Mind the Gap

Unwashed, Joyously, Poisoner, Prologue, Whiplash, Tangible, Blowhole, Tributes.

The bright thing is:
SUNLIGHT

PAGE 13
Pathfinder

White, Hazel, Purple, Russet, Khaki, Viridian, Gold, Aquamarine, Ultramarine, Magenta, Blue, Crimson, Lavender, Amber, Turquoise, Vermilion, Ochre, Scarlet

Sudoku

6	3	5	4	1	9	8	7	2
1	7	4	8	3	2	5	9	6
2	8	9	5	7	6	1	4	3
7	2	1	6	9	3	4	5	8
4	9	8	1	2	5	6	3	7
5	6	3	7	8	4	9	2	1
9	1	6	3	5	7	2	8	4
8	5	7	2	4	1	3	6	9
3	4	2	9	6	8	7	1	5

PAGE 14
Wrestle Table

The Assassin – Typhoon Terry; The Battling Acrobat – The Gretna Grappler; The Fightin' Titan – Lee Bruce; Pretty Boy – The Shark

PAGE 14
Lose a Letter

PAGE 15
Missing Links

PAGE 16
Word Builder

Blade, Bored, Abode, Above, Bravo, Bread, Double, Verbal, Adverb, Bolder, Rouble, Braved, Boulder, Durable, Laboured, Boulevard

Backwords

PAGE 17
Picture Pair
Pictures **1** and **2**

PAGE 17
Six Pack

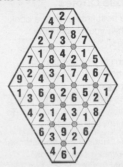

PAGE 18
Drop Quote

'If I have any beliefs about immortality, it is that certain dogs I have known will go to heaven, and very, very few persons.'

PAGE 19
Sudoku

3	6	5	2	1	4	8	7	9
1	9	7	6	8	5	4	2	3
4	2	8	7	3	9	5	1	6
2	7	1	4	9	3	6	5	8
6	4	3	5	7	8	2	9	1
5	8	9	1	6	2	7	3	4
7	3	2	9	4	6	1	8	5
8	5	6	3	2	1	9	4	7
9	1	4	8	5	7	3	6	2

Answers

PAGE 19
Mobile Quotes

"The best time to plan a book is while you're doing the dishes."

"I don't think necessity is the mother of invention – invention, in my opinion, arises directly from idleness, possibly also from laziness. To save oneself trouble."

"I like living. I have sometimes been wildly, despairingly, acutely miserable, racked with sorrow, but through it all I still know quite certainly that just to be alive is a grand thing."

Agatha Christie

PAGE 20
Alpha-Beater

Set Square

PAGE 21
Elimination

Satellites – Explorer, Iridium, Moon, Sputnik, Telstar
GREEN – Common, Inexperienced, Leafy, Naïve, Verdant
Stations – Euston, Marylebone, Paddington, Victoria, Waterloo
Door – Barn, Fire, Trap, Stable, Stage
Leftover: **FULL STOP**

PAGE 22
Kim's Game

Spot the Difference

PAGE 23
Memory Jog

1 Atlantia **2** Mercanton
3 Bunaria **4** Udolpho **5** Illyria
6 Dobravnia **7** Nubaria
8 Otranto

PAGE 24
Three to One

PAGE 25
Mini Jigsaw

Column, Errata, Margin, Letter, Format, Offset

PAGE 26
First Thoughts

PAGE 27
The Great Escape

PAGE 28
Sudoku

Arroword

PAGE 29
Prints Charming

A 9 **B** 14 **C** 7

Word Sleuth

Mystery word: **WOLF**

Answers

PAGE 30
Skeleton

PAGE 31
Logical

Charles, Wrexham, Carrot,
Oranges
Joy, Dundee, Peach, Beetroot
Robina, Lisburn, Hazelnut,
Cream

Knot or not?

Knot – **2** and **4** Not – **1** and **3**

PAGE 32
Jigsaw

PAGE 33
Pattern Maker

1 Square 3 (segments +1
each time) **2** Square 2 (pattern
rotates 90°, 4 non-standard
colours, 1 new each time)
3 Square 5 (each pattern is
symmetrical when rotated 180°)

PAGE 34
Elimination

Inventors – Dunlop, Edison,
Faraday, Marconi, Stephenson

Puzzle – Anagram,
Conundrum, Crossword,
Cryptogram, Riddle

Watercourses – Brook, Creek,
River, Rivulet, Stream

Hardware – Cable, Chip, Disk,
Key, Mouse

Remaining: **BUTTONHOLE**

Mix-up

PAGE 35
Add Up

1 96 2 63 3 84

PAGE 36
Fair Play

1 C3 2 C2 3 A2 4 A3 5 C1
6 C4 7 B3 8 A1 9 B4 10 B2

PAGE 37
Dilemma Fitword

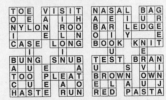

PAGE 38
Wheels & Cogs

Right dragon.

PAGE 38
Wheely Good

BLAME

BLUNDER

PAGE 39
Word Builder

Capes, Pears, Spare, Paste,
Sport, Prose, Potter, Scrape,
Operas, Pastor, Aspect,
Poster, Teapots, Toecaps,
Carpets, Protest, Seaport,
Protects, Spectator

PAGE 40
Mix & Match

PAGE 41
Killer Sudoku

8	2	7	1	6	4	3	9	5
1	3	6	9	8	5	7	4	2
5	9	4	3	2	7	8	6	1
3	8	2	6	9	1	5	7	4
6	1	5	4	7	2	9	8	3
4	7	9	8	5	3	1	2	6
2	5	8	7	3	6	4	1	9
9	6	1	5	4	8	2	3	7
7	4	3	2	1	9	6	5	8

Answers

PAGE 41
Lettersets

PAGE 42
Missing Links

PAGE 44
Square Eyes
The identical squares are a8 and d4

Memory Jog
1 Tomis 2 Illyria 3 Udolpho
4 Poseida 5 Mercanton
6 Forest 7 Alpathian mountains
8 Otranto

PAGE 45
Codeword

Boxwise
1 Que 2 Asy 3 Lum 4 Pre
5 Ens 6 Bar 7 Fer 8 Fil 9 Ter
10 Ret 11 Ail 12 Ing

PAGE 46
Number Jig

PAGE 47
Writing Wrongs
1 When the minute hand is on 6, the hour hand should be mid-way between the numbers, in this case between 12 and 1
2 The pound coin didn't become currency until 1983
3 Opposite sides of a die add up to 7, so 6 and 1 can't be adjacent
4 The queen is facing the wrong direction
5 The pennant at the top of the mast should be in the opposite direction – the wind is blowing from left to right, indicated by the billow in the sail

PAGE 48
Fitword

Leftover word: **SHIRK**

PAGE 49
Jigsaw

PAGE 50
Too Close a Shave
Reflection 9

It's Sound!

Bebop, Boogie, Calypso, Classical, Country, Folk, Garage, Gospel, Grunge, Heavy metal, Jazz, Jive, Opera, Punk, Swing

PAGE 51
Mix & Match

PAGE 52
Hide and Seek
1 c7 2 b4 3 a2 4 a6 5 f7 6 e3

Answers

PAGE 53
Dateline

6	7	6		2		7	7	6
2		1	0	4	4	0		4
3	5	1			9	7	2	9
1		2		2	6		6	7
	2	6	5	1	7	9	8	
4	2		1	0		0		2
9	0	8	5			1	2	6
4		6	3	8	9	4		2
9	1	3		3		3	4	8

Date: **26.5.1798** (introduction of income tax in Britain)

PAGE 54
Futoshiki

2	3	1
1	2	3
3	1	2

1	3	2
2	1	3
3	2	1

2	4	1	3
3	1	4	2
4	2	3	1
1	3	2	4

Number Jig

3		5	1	4	6	2		7
2	6	2	6		7	8	2	2
1	7	6	4		3	2	7	9
5	9	4		9	4	0	9	6
	2		6	5	7		8	
5	5	3	6	4		9	2	9
2	3	6	0		1	2	3	2
1	8	1	8		5	6	7	6
0		9	7	3	7	0		4

Leftover number: **7612**

PAGE 55
Codeword

PAGE 56
Arroword

Staircase

Curtain, Runner, Cistern, Keyhole, Blind, Pillow, Basin.

The household term is: **CUSHION**

PAGE 57
StepRiddle

Colts, Bolts, Belts, Beats, Bears, Beard

PAGE 58
Missing Links

PAGE 59
Backwords

PAGE 60
Dilemma Crossword

PAGE 61
Sudoku

3	1	8	2	9	4	6	7	5
5	9	4	6	8	7	3	2	1
2	6	7	1	5	3	8	9	4
4	2	9	3	6	5	7	1	8
1	7	6	8	4	2	9	5	3
8	3	5	9	7	1	4	6	2
7	4	3	5	1	9	2	8	6
6	5	2	7	3	8	1	4	9
9	8	1	4	2	6	5	3	7

Mobile Quotes

"The object of this competition is not to be mean to the losers but to find a winner. The process makes you mean because you get frustrated. Kids turn up unrehearsed, wearing the wrong clothes, singing out of tune and you can either say, 'Good job,' and patronise them or tell them the truth, and sometimes the truth is perceived as mean."

"I haven't done anything particularly harsh. Harshness to me is giving somebody false hopes and not following through. That's harsh. Telling some guy or some girl who've got zero talent that they have zero talent actually is a kindness."

"I do a couple of hundred press-ups a day but I haven't been to a gym in years."

Simon Cowell

Answers

PAGE 62
Alpha-Beater

```
E Y   B R A     A
P R O X Y   F J O R D
I   G   W   T   I
C O U G A R   T S A R
    R   Y   Q   I
M O T H   B U Z Z E R
V   I   E   Z   A
D E M O N   R E L I C
N     K E Y   E   Y
```

Set Square

7	×	3	−	9
+		×		+
5	+	8	+	6
÷		÷		×
2	×	4	÷	1

2	×	7	+	6
+		−		+
8	+	5	×	1
+		×		+
9	+	3	÷	4

PAGE 63
Elimination

Rainbow – Blue, Green, Red, Violet, Yellow

Songbirds – Lark, Thrush, Wagtail, Wren, Yellowhammer

Art – Acrylic, Brush, Canvas, Model, Pastel

Cartoon – Custard, Droopy, Pluto, Snoopy, Tintin

Leftover: **BLACK SWAN**

PAGE 64
Kim's Game

1 Hexagon, 'down' triangle
2 Pentagon, star 3 Cross tilted, red triangle now orange, red semicircle inverted

PAGE 65
Spot the Difference

PAGE 66
Face Facts

Air, Boat race, Clock, Confront, Dial, Display, Expression, Facade, Guise, Look, Manner, Mug, Mush, Phiz, Scowl, Side, Surface, Visage

Memory Quiz

1 Angels 2 Red 3 2006
4 Andrex 5 HMRC (Her Majesty's Revenue and Customs) 6 Green 7 Trumpet 8 Occurrence

PAGE 67
Three to One

PAGE 68
Kakuro

5	1		6	9	8	7
2	3	4	1	8	7	9	5	6
6	8	3	9			9	7

Mini Jigsaw

Recipe, Picnic, Course, Ration, Simmer, Buffet

PAGE 69
First Thoughts

```
C H I L D   B O S O M
O   N   R   I   P   A
M A N S I O N   O L D
E   R   V   G   T   E
D I F F E R E N T   B
Y     I   I   E   E B
    G U N P O W D E R
G   H   O   P     E
O U T   B R I T T L E
L   E   L   U   A C
F O R C E   M A R C H
```

PAGE 70
Phone China

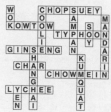

```
W     C H O P S U E Y
O   O     A       M
K O W T O W   M   S A
  O     L   T Y P H O O N
G I N S E N G   A   N D
  A     H     K     A
  C H A R   C H O W M E I N
  A   N     U       I
L Y C H E E   Q U A T
E       A     U
N       I     T
```

Futoshiki

2	3	1
1	2	3
3	1	2

3	1	2
1	2	3
2	3	1

2	1	3	4
1	2	4	3
4	3	2	1
3	4	1	2

PAGE 71
Sudoku

4	7	1	6	9	3	8	2	5
8	6	2	5	1	4	7	9	3
3	5	9	7	2	8	4	1	6
7	1	5	9	8	6	2	3	4
6	2	3	4	7	1	5	8	9
9	8	4	3	5	2	1	6	7
5	4	8	2	3	9	6	7	1
1	9	7	8	6	5	3	4	2
2	3	6	1	4	7	9	5	8

Answers

PAGE 71
Arroword

PAGE 72
Key Signatures
A 11 B 5 C 2

Word Sleuth
Mystery word. **BATH**

PAGE 73
Skeleton

PAGE 74
Logical
Joan, Rich, £50,000, Rucksack
Nazreen, Goldie, £100,000,
Rip-proof fabric
Phyllis, Luca, £150,000,
Safety glass

Knot or Not?
Knot – **2** and **3** Not – **1** and **4**

PAGE 75
Jigsaw

PAGE 76
Elimination
WHITE – Bread, Dwarf, Gold,
Noise, Tie

Tools – Chisel, Plane, Saw,
Spanner, Wrench

Adjectives – First, Further,
Purple, Quick, Sad

Fabric – Linen, Moleskin,
Polyester, Satin, Tweed

Remaining: **HOUSEWORK**

Mix-up

PAGE 77
StepRiddle
Glass, Class, Crass, Cross,
Crows, Crowd

PAGE 78
A Matter of Course
1 B1 **2** A3 **3** C4 **4** C1 **5** B4
6 A2 **7** B2 **8** C2 **9** A4 **10** C3

Add Up
1 68 **2** 82 **3** 118

PAGE 80
Dilemma Fitword

PAGE 81
Wheels & Cogs
Recharger

Out of Hand

Bag, Ball, Brake, Cart, Cuffs,
Gronade, Kerchief, Made,
Maiden, Out, Over, Picked,
Pump, Rail, Saw, Set, Shake,
Some, Spring, Stand, Towel,
Writing

PAGE 82
Mix & Match

PAGE 83
Killer Sudoku

8	9	3	5	6	2	7	4	1
6	7	1	3	4	9	5	8	2
2	5	4	8	7	1	9	3	6
9	6	2	1	5	4	3	7	8
4	1	5	7	3	8	2	6	9
3	8	7	9	2	6	1	5	4
1	3	6	4	9	7	8	2	5
5	2	8	6	1	3	4	9	7
7	4	9	2	8	5	6	1	3

Answers

PAGE 83
Lettersets

```
S C R A M   M A Y
  H E W   R A C E
P A C E   A L M S
E R A   F I L E
W   P R U N E   J
  S T I R   A P E
T A U T   A B U T
O G R E   I L L
T E E   S M E L T
```

PAGE 84
Missing Links

```
  P A L M   D U C K
S   F   O   E   H
W E T   R U B B I S H
I   E   A   T   L   I
M A R B L E   F L A G
M   U   A     A   H
I R O N   B A R R E L
N   N   E   P   I   A
G R I N D E R   G U N
  O   G   O   H   D
  K N E E   N O T E
```

PAGE 86
Set Square

1	+	2	×	3
+		×		×
6	×	5	−	4
÷		−		−
7	+	8	+	9

6	+	4	−	7
+		×		+
8	×	5	÷	2
+		−		÷
1	×	3	+	9

Square Eyes
The identical squares are
b1 and **f9**

PAGE 87
Codeword

```
E   S   I   O R B   S   G   A
D E C O D E D   I M P A L E D
I   U   E   E   R   A   I   H
T O M C A T   F O R C I B L E
E   E   L   O       I       L
D E V I L R Y   C O N J U R E
  I   Y - S   L   G - N   N
D A D O   S T E A K   F I A T
I   E   P   E   U   B   F
S P O I L E R   S P L A Y E D
L   A     E   O     O   E
O C C A S I O N   A W O K E N
D   O   T   U   A   O   I   U
G L A Z I E R   S Q U A L I D
E   X   C   S A P   T   T   E
```

```
Q I W M G F U S J R V H E
O K Y T N Z B L C X D A P
```

PAGE 88
Boxwise

1 Tur **2** Bot **3** Tom **4** Pot **5** Een
6 Ato **7** Ent **8** Fil **9** Mic **10** Rap
11 Per **12** Ter

PAGE 88
Number Jig

```
9 2 3   9 5 2 3 2
1 5 4 8 4   4 1 2
2 5 6   1 2 7 8 6
3 8 9 6 0 4 2   9
  7   0   8   5
4   9 8 3 0 2 0 4
1 4 5 3 1   1 4 2
6 5 6   2 0 7 3 4
9 0 2 4 6   3 1 6
```

PAGE 89
Fitword

```
C U S P   S L I P
O   P   O   O   A
W H O   N E W E R
L   O   E   E   T
  O F F   T R U E
P   A G O   D
H O A X   G A P
O   W   G   B   H
N I F T Y   A R E
E   U   M   C   M
D O L E   S K E P
```

Leftover word: **FEN**

PAGE 90
Sudoku

4	3	1	2
1	2	3	4
2	1	4	3
3	4	2	1

4	3	2	1
2	1	4	3
3	4	1	2
1	2	3	4

4	2	1	3
3	1	4	2
1	3	2	4
2	4	3	1

Logical
Christine, Liverpool, steward
Jo, Leeds, waitress
Penny, London, chef

PAGE 91
Jigsaw

```
C   V E T   K
T A X I   O M I T
N   S I X   W
S E A T   I R I S
A   D A N C E   T
R U M   U   P E A
C   I N T E R   T
A C R E   A I D E
S   A W A R E   M
T U B   D   V I E
I   L O C S E   N
C R E W   E D I T
I   N O W   D
O N C E   E W E R
G   R O D   A
```

PAGE 92
For Arms
Transfer **3**

Coasting Along

```
B R E M O R C S A
O L T D R N D C Y
N E A M Y U G A T
D H G C N R S R E
U S R B K E O B L
D U A R H P O O S
N R M T H B O R I
A T O T A Y T O L
L R U N C D L U L
O N A I R N G I
S P L A R G S H M
```

Blackpool, Cromer, Dunbar,
Largs, Llandudno, Margate,
Millisle, Nairn, Oban, Portrush,
Rhyl, Rothesay, Ryde,
Scarborough, Southport

PAGE 93
Mix & Match

```
L A N G U I S H   C H E F
E   A   G   U   S   O   A
V I T A L   B I T U M E N
E   U   Y   D   A   E   F
L A R K   B U L G A R I A
A     D   E   G     N   B
P O L L E N   N E S S I E
R   E     A   R   P
O C C U P A N T   L A V A
S   R   S   G   I   N   L
P L A C E B O   T W I S T
E   M   T   R   C   E   E
R O P E   B A C H E L O R
```

PAGE 94
Futoshiki

2	3	1
3	1	2
1	2	3

3	2	1
2	1	3
1	3	2

4	1	2	3
1	3	4	2
2	4	3	1
3	2	1	4

Answers

PAGE 95
Dateline

Date: **22.6.1377**
(Richard II became king of England)

PAGE 96
Codeword

PAGE 97
Arroword

StepRiddle

Noise, Poise, Prise, Prose, Prone, Prong

PAGE 98
Staircase

Clause, Mandate, Cabal, Edict, Junta, Charter, Budget.

The politics term is: **CABINET**

PAGE 100
Mind the Gap

Hiccups, Poppies, Renewal, Plodder, Impeach, Pudding, Postage.

The jewellery word is:
PENDANT

Pathfinder

Sailing, Triathlon, Handball, Hockey, Weightlifting, Rowing, Wrestling, Diving, Softball, Athletics, Shooting, Gymnastics, Football, Judo, Volleyball

PAGE 101
Sudoku

Lose a Letter

PAGE 102
Pic and Mix

André – scones; George – sandwiches; Keiko – samosas; Tanita – shortbread

PAGE 102
Word Builder

Repel, Elope, Reply, Slope, Peers, Strop, Prose, Repose, Pester, Sleepy, Petrol, Osprey, Portly, Poster, Retypes, Leprosy, Steeply, Polyester

PAGE 103
Missing Links

PAGE 104
Backwords

PAGE 105
Picture Pair
Pictures **1** and **5**

Six Pack

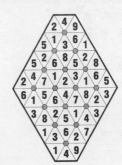

Answers

PAGE 106
Drop Quote

'Seeing a murder on television can help work off one's antagonisms. And if you haven't any antagonisms, the commercials will give you some.'

Mobile Quotes

"Experience is a great advantage. The problem is that when you get the experience, you're too damned old to use it."

"New Yorkers love it when you spill your guts out there. Spill your guts at Wimbledon and they make you stop and clean it up."

"Rather than viewing a brief relapse back to inactivity as a failure, treat it as a challenge and try to get back on track as soon as possible."

Jimmy Connors

PAGE 107
Dilemma Crossword

PAGE 108
Sudoku

7	2	1	4	8	6	9	5	3
8	6	4	9	3	5	1	7	2
5	3	9	1	7	2	6	4	8
4	5	2	8	6	1	3	9	7
6	9	7	2	4	3	5	8	1
1	8	3	5	9	7	4	2	6
9	4	6	3	2	8	7	1	5
3	1	8	7	5	4	2	6	9
2	7	5	6	1	9	8	3	4

Alpha-Beater

PAGE 109
Set Square

9	−	7	+	3
−		−		×
6	÷	1	+	5
×		+		−
2	×	8	÷	4

3	×	7	−	8
+		−		+
9	−	5	+	4
−		+		+
6	×	1	+	2

Elimination

Furniture – Chair, Divan, Dresser, Table, Wardrobe

TWINE – Cord, Rope, String, Thread, Yarn

Yellow – Banana, Canary, Daffodil, Lemon, Yolk

SCOTLAND – Bagpipes, Haggis, Kilt, Shortbread, Whisky

Remaining: **BALLROOM**

PAGE 111
Kim's Game

1 Relay runner, tennis player
2 Golfer, Baseball player
3 Skier's pole missing, green martial arts suit purple, boxers reversed.

PAGE 111
Making a Splash

Armbands, Bikini, Butterfly, Costume, Crawl, Flippers, Goggles, Lifeguard, Medley, Pool, Sea, Snorkel, Trunks

PAGE 112
Three to One

PAGE 113
Kakuro

7	9		6	4	9	8	
9	8	5	1	2	7	4	6	3
	9	3	1	8		2	1

Mini Jigsaw

Radium, Nickel, Carbon, Copper, Silver, Helium

PAGE 114
First Thoughts

Answers

PAGE 115
Memory Quiz
1 Green **2** Precede **3** 5
4 June (27) **5** The Queen's
Silver Jubilee year, 1977
6 Fairy **7** Burgundy **8** 3

PAGE 116
Court Out

PAGE 117
Futoshiki

Sudoku

4	1	2	7	9	3	6	5	8
5	8	9	1	6	2	3	7	4
3	6	7	5	8	4	9	2	1
7	9	3	4	5	1	2	8	6
6	4	1	8	2	7	5	9	3
2	5	8	6	3	9	1	4	7
9	7	4	3	1	5	8	6	2
1	2	6	9	4	8	7	3	5
8	3	5	2	7	6	4	1	9

PAGE 118
Arroword

Word Sleuth
Mystery word: **ARTS**

PAGE 119
Droid Rage
A 3 B 10 C 12

PAGE 120
Vowel Play

Logical
Phil Lloyd, doctor, US Dawn
Powers, zoologist, NZ
Robbie McGrath, film-maker,
India

PAGE 121
Skeleton

PAGE 122
Knot or Not?
Knot – **1** and **4** Not – **2** and **3**

PAGE 122
Jigsaw

PAGE 123
Pattern Maker
1 Square 5 2 Square 3
3 Square 2

PAGE 124
Elimination
BABY – Bush, Cry, Jelly, Test-
tube, War

Church – Aisle, Altar, Apse,
Font, Nave

Flowers – Crocus, Hyacinth,
Iris, Rose, Tulip

PIANO – Grand, Key, Stool,
Tuner, Upright

Remaining: **THUNDERBOLT**

Mix-up

PAGE 126
Forefully Good
1 C2 **2** A1 **3** B4 **4** C1 **5** A2
6 C4 **7** B1 **8** C3 **9** A4 **10** B3

Answers

PAGE 126
Add Up

1 95 **2** 75 **3** 86

PAGE 128
Dilemma Fitword

```
S A Y   A P H I D     P A P E R   B U S
A   E   I   A   I     L   A   O   U   C
L A S E R   T O R     E A R   L A Y E R
A     Y   C   G       A   L   E       A
D U P E   S H O E     D R O P   S H O P
  I       E           U       U       O
F A T E   A T O P     F I R E   S T U B
R   C   A     L       F   F   F   U
A S H   C O Y P U     O T H E R   O A R
  I E   I   A M       A   I E   O K
L U R I D   P U B     T O P   E X T R A
```

PAGE 129
Wheels & Cogs

Ball 2

Sock 'n' Sole

Brogue, Clog, Espadrille,
Flip-flop, High heel, Loafer,
Moccasin, Mule, Oxford,
Plimsoll, Pump, Sandal,
Slingback, Slipper, Sneaker,
Stiletto, Trainer

PAGE 130
Word Builder

Lucre, Ounce, Clone, Close,
Clues, Scour, Curse, Scone,
Uncles, Rescue, Screen,
Consul, Crones, Source,
Course, Ulcers, Counsel,
Censure, Encores, Enclosure

StepRiddle

Black, Slack, Stack, Stick,
Stink, Sting

PAGE 131
Killer Sudoku

```
1 5 4 8 9 7 2 3 6
8 3 2 6 5 1 4 9 7
7 6 9 2 4 3 8 5 1
6 1 7 9 8 5 3 2 4
2 9 8 4 3 6 7 1 5
5 4 3 1 7 2 9 6 8
3 2 5 7 6 8 1 4 9
4 8 1 5 2 9 6 7 3
9 7 6 3 1 4 5 8 2
```

Lettersets

```
P I G   P A S T E
E L U D E   H O D
A L L   L   O D D
T   P A T H W A Y
  J   R   E   Y
S U L K I N G   M
L I E   D   E Y E
I C E   L I N E R
D E R B Y   E W E
```

PAGE 132
Mix & Match

```
S C A R A B   G L A N C E
  R   E   U   A   B   H
S O Y A   M I S C H I E F
  W   L   P       O   R
A S P I R E   C A R R O T
    S   R   R       O
S P O T   C H A   C I T E
  U   A   A   B   H
D R A W E R   A R E N A S
  S   E   P   R   T
F U L L S T O P   I O T A
  I   S   E   L   S
E T C H E D   E T H I C S
```

PAGE 133
Missing Links

```
  S C A R   L E F T
U   A   O   A   O
M A N   G A S T R I C
B   A   U   T   C   A
R O L L E R   B E A R
E   I       A
L A C E   S I G N A L
L   H   F   N   O
A R A B I A N   B U S
  R   L   E   L   S
  S T E M   R E E L
```

PAGE 134
Set Square

```
6 × 5 − 7       9 − 4 + 8
+     ×         ×   +   +
8 − 3 × 1       2 × 1 + 7
÷     −   +     ÷   ÷   ÷
2 + 9 − 4       6 + 5 − 3
```

PAGE 135
Codeword

```
A   R   B   O R B   S   I   P
B R O I L E D   E Q U A T O R
S   T   O E   L   R   A   E
O P A Q U E   F L A G S H I P
R   S   A   E       E       E
B A L L O O N   S T R I K E R
  I   N   S   C   Y   H   L
J U M P   S W A R M   W A X Y
U   B   S   E     I   A   K
B L O A T E R   P E N S I V E
I   E   T       G       E
L U K E W A R M   T U R N I P
A   I   A   U   A   L   A
N A T U R A L   G L A Z I E R
T   E   D   E G O   R   L   T
```

```
U Z J H C Q W O A M V Y N
L K R P F G I D B E S X T
```

PAGE 136
Boxwise

1 Raf **2** Fia **3** Sco **4** Tri **5** Fle
6 Urs **7** Bal **8** Sal **9** Ine
10 Sam **11** Ple **12** Ads

Number Jig

```
7 7 7   5 0 1 8 1
5 6 2 3 0   2 1 3
1 2 4   9 5 4 3 6
4 2 9 3 1 6 7   9
  7   4 2   7
5   3 2 4 9 7 6 1
7 1 0 9 0   4 2 3
4 2 0   2 5 2 2 5
9 3 0 8 9   1 1 4
```

PAGE 137
Who and Where?

The celebrities, in order,
are: Clint Eastwood, David
Cameron, Gillian Anderson,
Gordon Brown, Julie Walters,
Noel Edmonds, Paul Merton,
Robbie Williams, Robert De
Niro, Ronan Keating, Rowan
Atkinson, Tina Turner, Tom
Cruise, Victoria Beckham

Answers

PAGE 138
Fitword

Leftover word: **HARM**

PAGE 139
Sudoku

Logical

Ashley, School for Scoundrels, boys

Georgia, School of Rock, girls

Tommy, School of Hard Knocks, Mixed

PAGE 140
Jigsaw

PAGE 141
Mix & Match

PAGE 142
Hide and Seek

1 d7 2 f5 3 d1 4 a3 5 a6 6 c1

PAGE 143
Dateline

Date: **31.8.1972**
(Mark Spitz won five of the seven gold medals he won in total at the Munich Olympics)

PAGE 144
Sweet Success

Piece **9**

Futoshiki

1	3	2

2	1	3

2	1	3

1	3	2

3	2	1

3	2	1

4	2	1	3
1	4	3	2
3	1	2	4
2	3	4	1

PAGE 145
Number Jig

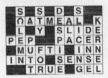

Leftover number: **4215**

Arroword

PAGE 146
Codeword

PAGE 148
Staircase

Fustian, Alpaca, Gauze, Canvas, Merino, Nankeen, Twill.

The fabric is: **FLANNEL**

Answers

PAGE 148
Mind the Gap

Expunge, Caboose, Torches, Agitate, Fishery, Scandal, Epitome, Stipend.

The shaded word is: **PORTRAIT**

PAGE 150
Pathfinder

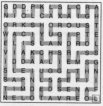

Loafing, Shiftless, Enervated, Sluggish, Lackadaisical, Idle, Indolent, Impassive, Work-shy, Languorous, Torpid, Remiss, Lethargic, Lax, Slack, Plodding

Sudoku

PAGE 151
Lose a Letter

PAGE 151
Word Builder

Lupin, Liner, Until, Burnt, Prune, Brine, Turnip, Lupine, Punier, Unripe, Punter, Line-up, Tribune, Turbine, Blunter, Blueprint

PAGE 152
Missing Links

PAGE 153
Backwords

PAGE 154
Picture Pair

Pictures **2** and **5**

PAGE 154
Stage Directions

Brigadoon, Cabaret, Camelot, Carousel, Cats, Chess, Chicago, Evita, Gigi, Godspell, Grease, Hairspray, Oklahoma!, Oliver!, Tommy

PAGE 155
Six Pack

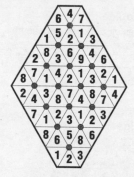

Drop Quote

'The whole problem with the world is that fools and fanatics are always so certain of themselves, but wiser people so full of doubts.'

Bertrand Russell

Answers

PAGE 156
Dilemma Crossword

PAGE 157
Mobile Quotes

"I think the worst woman that ever existed would have made a man of very passable reputation – they are all better than us and their faults such as they are must originate with ourselves."

"I have great hopes that we shall love each other all our lives as much as if we had never married at all."

"America is a model of force and freedom and moderation – with all the coarseness and rudeness of its people."

"Always laugh when you can. It is cheap medicine."

Lord Byron

Sudoku

6	1	8	7	2	9	3	5	4
3	2	5	1	8	4	7	6	9
4	7	9	6	5	3	1	2	8
2	4	6	9	3	7	8	1	5
8	3	7	2	1	5	9	4	6
5	9	1	4	6	8	2	3	7
1	8	2	5	7	6	4	9	3
9	5	3	8	4	2	6	7	1
7	6	4	3	9	1	5	8	2

PAGE 158
Alpha-Beater

Set Square

2	×	8	−	3
×		×		+
9	+	1	−	7
÷		+		÷
6	−	4	×	5

9	×	2	÷	3
+		+		×
4	×	5	−	8
−		−		
6	+	1	+	7

PAGE 159
Elimination

Toys – Doll, Kite, Rattle, Skates, Teddy

Reptiles – Crocodile, Iguana, Lizard, Snake, Turtle

Music genres – Blues, House, Jazz, Reggae, Rock

FLY – Butter, Dragon, Fire, Green, Hover

Remaining: HOPSCOTCH

PAGE 161
Three to One

PAGE 163
Kakuro

7	9		3	1	8	9		
9	8	4	1	2	7	5	6	3
	8	6	4	9		2	1	

Mini Jigsaw

Weepie, Studio, Comedy, Sequel, Camera, Biopic

PAGE 164
First Thoughts

PAGE 165
Verse Strings

Futoshiki

3	1	2
2	3	1
1	2	3

1	3	2
3	2	1
2	1	3

4	1	3	2
2	3	4	1
3	2	1	4
1	4	2	3

Answers

PAGE 166
Sudoku

4	5	9	6	2	1	7	8	3
2	7	1	4	3	8	9	5	6
8	3	6	7	9	5	1	2	4
6	4	5	1	8	7	3	9	2
1	2	3	9	5	4	6	7	8
9	8	7	3	6	2	4	1	5
3	9	8	5	1	6	2	4	7
5	1	4	2	7	3	8	6	9
7	6	2	8	4	9	5	3	1

Arroword

PAGE 167
Vowel Play

Logical

Ed, Rex, Pug, Chicken
Ged, Sam, Mongrel, Tuna
Ted, Ben, Labrador, Steak

PAGE 168
Pattern Maker

1 Square 4 **2** Square 1
3 Square 3

PAGE 170
Dilemma Fitword

PAGE 171
Word Builder

Lance, React, Creel, Clone,
Crane, Eclat, Oracle, Claret,
Cornet, Trance, Carton, Nectar,
Cleaner, Central, Elector,
Lectern, Treacle, Electron,
Carotene, Relocate, Tolerance

StepRiddle

Quite, Suite, Spite, Spate,
Spare, Spars

PAGE 172
Missing Links

PAGE 173
Codeword

PAGE 174
One on One

PAGE 175
Set Square

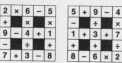